J.

ON
c.D.

DISCARDED

DISCARDED

OPTICAL OCEANOGRAPHY

Elsevier Oceanography Series

OPTICAL OCEANOGRAPHY

BY

N. G. JERLOV

Professor of Physical Oceanography
University of Copenhagen
Copenhagen

ELSEVIER PUBLISHING COMPANY
AMSTERDAM — LONDON — NEW YORK
1968

ELSEVIER PUBLISHING COMPANY
335 JAN VAN GALENSTRAAT, P.O. BOX 211, AMSTERDAM
THE NETHERLANDS

ELSEVIER PUBLISHING COMPANY LTD.
BARKING, ESSEX, ENGLAND

AMERICAN ELSEVIER PUBLISHING COMPANY, INC.
52 VANDERBILT AVENUE
NEW YORK, NEW YORK 10017

147270

LIBRARY OF CONGRESS CATALOG CARD NUMBER 68–12475

WITH 83 ILLUSTRATIONS AND 28 TABLES

COPYRIGHT © 1968 BY ELSEVIER PUBLISHING COMPANY, AMSTERDAM

ALL RIGHTS RESERVED
THIS BOOK OR ANY PART THEREOF
MUST NOT BE REPRODUCED IN ANY FORM
WITHOUT THE WRITTEN PERMISSION OF THE PUBLISHER,
ELSEVIER PUBLISHING COMPANY, AMSTERDAM, THE NETHERLANDS

PRINTED IN THE NETHERLANDS

To Elvi

PREFACE

The purpose of this book is to bring together into a comprehensive review what is known about the optics of the sea. The reader will find that the physical aspect of the problem and its relationship to oceanography is predominant. Some emphasis is laid on the characteristics of instruments and on their capacity for providing adequate definitions of measured quantities.

Thermodynamics has been considered to lie outside the scope of the book. Furthermore, "Underwater photography and television" have not been dealt with since excellent reviews of these chiefly technical subjects have recently been published.

The monograph is presented with the reservation that it is not a complete description of all theories of the optics of the sea and does not cover all research in the field. The author, nevertheless, hopes that it will be useful as a reference book and that it can answer questions which confront the student or the specialist.

I am indebted to friends and colleagues all over the world for their support of this work, and in particular to Professor E. Steemann Nielsen and to Drs. Joachim Joseph and John Tyler for stimulating criticism and advice. I also want to express my sincere thanks to the staff of the Institute of Physical Oceanography, Copenhagen, for their unstinting cooperation.

Nils Jerlov

CONTENTS

But where shall wisdom be found?
And where is the place of understanding?

The deep saith, "It is not in me".
And the sea saith, "It is not with me".

(*The Book of Job*, 8:12, 14)

CHAPTER 1

INTRODUCTION

NATURE OF THE SUBJECT

Optical oceanography considers the sea from an optical standpoint and is generally considered as a special branch of oceanography. The subject is chiefly physical, and aspires to employ strict definitions of the quantities measured. Underwater optics have wide applications in oceanography and related fields, and attract growing attention to the possibility of characterizing water masses by means of their optical properties.

The various dissolved and particulate substances present in sea water largely determine its optical properties. It is a primary task of optical oceanography to find out which ingredients are optically active and to study their optical behaviour. This presupposes an intimate knowledge of the properties of the water itself as a pure liquid.

An exchange of ideas and techniques between oceanography and meteorology is important. Both fields have an interest in the physical processes occurring at the sea surface which determine the interchange of energy between the atmosphere and the sea. On the other hand, the propagation of light in the atmosphere and in the sea is dominated by different physical processes. The atmosphere is primarily a scattering medium whereas in the ocean absorption as well as scattering plays an essential role. It has long been known that the total radiant energy from sun and sky loses half of its value in the first half meter of water, owing chiefly to strong absorption in the infra-red.

HISTORICAL NOTE

Though a detailed historical perspective lies outside the purview of this introduction, some highlights in the pre-war development of underwater optics may be mentioned. The progress of research has been intimately connected with the evolution of instrumental technique. For the earliest measurements, only photographic methods were available. The initial study of radiant energy dates back to 1885 when Fol and Sarasin exposed photographic plates in the Mediterranean off the Côte d'Azur. It merits attention that KNUDSEN (1922), by using a submerged spectrograph together with a photographic recording method, was successful in measuring spectral radiance at different levels in the sea.

The introduction of photoelectric cells for marine observations (SHELFORD and GAIL, 1922) revolutionized optical technique. In the 1930's much pioneer work was done on the design and use of radiance and irradiance meters (ATKINS and POOLE, 1933; CLARKE, 1933; UTTERBACK and BOYLE, 1933; PETTERSSON and LANDBERG, 1934; JERLOV and LILJEQUIST, 1938; TAKENOUTI, 1940; and WHITNEY, 1941). PETTERSSON (1934) also devised the first examples of in situ beam transmittance and scattering meters. KALLE (1938) obtained important results on the significance of soluble yellow matter for the transmission of light and for the colour of the sea. The study of particle distribution in the deep sea by means of a scattering meter is based on his original method. Finally, there is the important paper by LE GRAND (1939), which presents an analysis of methods employed in underwater optics together with deductions of fundamental laws.

Research spanning three decades has yielded surprisingly few results on the penetration of light in offshore waters. This is partially due to the difficulties involved in measuring with broad filters. Since 1955, however, the situation has completely changed, due to the introduction of photomultiplier tubes and interference filters. This technique, which enables us to study all optical parameters with a high accuracy, paved the way for a rapid development. Another strong impetus is provided by the invention of the laser, which is turning out to be a profitable tool in oceanographic optics. The advent of these tools has started a new epoque in the domain.

TERMINOLOGY

It was recognized by the Committee on Radiant Energy in the Sea (of the International Association of Physical Oceanography, IAPO) that a firm basis of definitions is imperative in optical oceanography. The definitions recommended by the Committee follow to some extent those published by the Commission Internationale d'Éclairage (Paris, 1957) and the International Dictionary of Physics and Electronics (New York, 1956); in addition, adequate definitions are introduced for the great number of terms specific for optics of the sea. The Committee has considered it beyond its scope to find a purely logical approach to the difficult definitions of such fundamental concepts as transmission, scattering and reflection. Those who want to dig deeper into the problems of definition are referred to an interpretation by PREISENDORFER (1960).

General principles

Some basic principles in the standard terminology are as follows. When dealing with radiant energy from sun and sky, the terms radiance and irradiance are considered to be fundamental; the concept of radiant intensity, which refers to point sources, has less application. Attenuation is preferred to extinction for representing the combined process of absorption and scattering. Meters are used after the quantity measured, e.g., radiance meter, irradiance meter, scatterance meter and beam transmittance meter (formerly transparency meter).

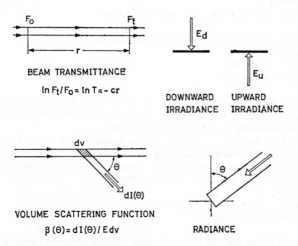

Fig.1. Sketches complementing the definition of quantities and properties.

The terms transparency and turbidity are not given strict definition; they are still used as rough indicators of the optical properties of water.

The list of terms and symbols for fundamental quantities, properties of the sea and instruments is presented below. The sketches in Fig.1 are a complement to the definitions, and also bring out the essential features of the instrumental design.

Definitions

Fundamental quantities

Wavelength. The distance between two successive points of a periodic wave in the direction of propagation, for which the oscillation has the same phase.

Note: The wavelength of monochromatic radiant energy depends on the refractive index of the medium. Unless otherwise stated, values of wavelengths are those in air.

  Symbol: λ
  Unit: m $1 \text{ nm} = 1 \text{ m}\mu = 10^{-9}\text{m}$

Sun zenith distance. The angle between the zenith and the sun's disc.
  Symbol: i

Quantity of radiant energy. Quantity of energy transferred by radiation.
  Symbol: Q
  Unit: joule, J; erg $1 \text{ erg} = 10^{-7} \text{ joule.}$

Radiant flux. The time rate of flow of radiant energy.
  Symbol: F
  Unit: watt, W
  Relation: $F = Q/t$

Radiant intensity (of a source in a given direction). The radiant flux emitted by a source, or by an element of a source, in an infinitesimal cone containing the given direction, divided by the solid angle of that cone.

Note: For a source which is not a point source: The quotient of the radiant flux received at an elementary surface by the solid angle which this surface subtends at any point of the source, when this quotient is taken to the limit as the distance between the surface and the source is increased.

  Symbol: I
  Unit: watt per steradian, W/sr
  Relation: $I = \mathrm{d}F/\mathrm{d}\omega$

Radiance. Radiant flux per unit solid angle per unit projected area of a surface.
  Symbol: L

Unit: watt per square metre and per steradian, W/m² sr
Relation: $L = \mathrm{d}^2 F/\mathrm{d}A \cos \varepsilon \, \mathrm{d}\omega$

Irradiance (at a point of a surface). The radiant flux incident on an infinitesimal element of surface containing the point under consideration, divided by the area of that element.
Symbol: E
Unit: watt per square metre, W/m²
Relation: $E = \mathrm{d}F/\mathrm{d}A$

Downward irradiance. The radiant flux on an infinitesimal element of the upper face (0–180°) of a horizontal surface containing the point being considered, divided by the area of that element.
Symbol: E_d
Unit: watt per square metre, W/m²
Relation: $E_d = \mathrm{d}F/\mathrm{d}A$

Upward irradiance. The radiant flux incident on an infinitesimal element of the lower face (180–360°) of a horizontal surface containing the point being considered, divided by the area of that element.
Symbol: E_u
Unit: watt per square metre, W/m²
Relation: $E_u = \mathrm{d}F/\mathrm{d}A$

Irradiance on a vertical plane. The radiant flux on an infinitesimal element of a vertical surface (90°) containing the point under consideration, divided by the area of that element.
Symbol: E_h
Unit: watt per square metre, W/m²
Relation: $E_h = \mathrm{d}F/\mathrm{d}A$

Irradiation (at a point of a surface). The product of an irradiance and its duration.
Symbol: —
Unit: joule per square metre, J/m²
Relation: $\mathrm{d}Q/\mathrm{d}A = \int E \, \mathrm{d}t$

Radiant emittance (at a point of a surface). The radiant flux emitted by an infinitesimal element of surface containing the point under consideration, divided by the area of that element.
Symbol: M
Unit: watt per square metre, W/m²
Relation: $M = \mathrm{d}F/\mathrm{d}A$

Spectral distribution curve of a radiometric quantity such as radiant flux, radiance, etc. Curve representing the spectral concentration of the quantity as a function of wavelength (or frequency).

Scalar irradiance. The integral of a radiance distribution at a point over all directions about the point.

Symbol: E_o

Unit: watt per square metre, W/m²

Relation: $E_o = \int_{4\pi} L \, d\omega$

Spherical irradiance. Limit of the ratio of radiant flux onto a spherical surface to the area of the surface, as the radius of the sphere tends toward zero with its centre fixed.

Symbol: E_s

Unit: watt per square metre, W/m²

Relation: $E_s = F_r/4\pi r^2$

where F_r is the radiant flux onto the sphere of radius r.

$E_s = \frac{1}{4} \cdot E_o$

Properties of the sea

Reflectance. The ratio of the reflected radiant flux to the incident radiant flux.

Symbol: ρ

Relation: $\rho = F_r/F_o$

Irradiance ratio (reflectance). The ratio of the upward to the downward irradiance at a depth in the sea.

Symbol: R

Relation: $R = E_u/E_d$

Transmittance. The ratio of the transmitted radiant flux to the incident radiant flux (in either irradiance or radiance form).

Symbol: T

Relation: $T = F_t/F_o$

Beam transmittance. The transmittance for a beam the diameter of which is small compared to its length.

Relation for homogeneous medium: $ln\, T = -cr$

Absorptance. The ratio of the radiant flux lost from a beam by means of absorption, to the incident flux.

Symbol: A

Relation: $A = F_a/F_o$

Scatterance. The ratio of the radiant flux scattered from a beam, to the incident flux.

Symbol: B

Relation: $B = F_b/F_o$

Forward scatterance. The ratio of the radiant flux scattered through angles $0-90°$ from a beam, to the incident flux.

Symbol: B_f

Backward scatterance. The ratio of the radiant flux scattered through angles $90-180°$ from a beam, to the incident flux.

    Symbol: B_b

Attenuance. The ratio of the radiant flux lost from a beam by means of absorption and scattering, to the incident flux.

    Symbol: C

    Relation: $C = F_c/F_o$

              $1-C = (1-A)(1-B) = T$

Absorption coefficient. The internal absorptance of an infinitesimally thin layer of the medium normal to the beam, divided by the thickness (Δr) of the layer.

    Symbol: a

    Unit: m^{-1}

    Relation: $a = -\Delta A/\Delta r = -\Delta F/F \, \Delta r$

    For homogeneous medium: $a \, r = -\, ln(1-A)$

Volume scattering function. The radiant intensity (from a volume element in a given direction) per unit of irradiance on the volume and per unit volume.

    Symbol: $\beta(\theta)$

    Unit: m^{-1}

    Relation: $\beta(\theta) = dI(\theta)/E \, dv$

(Total) scattering coefficient. The internal scatterance of an infinitesimally thin layer of the medium normal to the beam, divided by the thickness (Δr) of the layer.

    Symbol: b

    Unit: m^{-1}

    Relation: $b = -\Delta B/\Delta r = -\Delta F/F \, \Delta r$

              $b = \int_{4\pi} \beta(\theta) d\omega = 2\pi \int_0^\pi \beta(\theta) \sin\theta \, d\theta$

    For homogeneous medium: $b \, r = -\, ln(1-B)$

Forward scattering coefficient. The coefficient which relates to forward scatterance.

    Symbol: b_f

    Unit: m^{-1}

    Relation: $b_f = 2\pi \int_0^{\frac{1}{2}\pi} \beta(\theta) \sin\theta \, d\theta$

    For homogeneous medium: $b_f r = -ln(1-B_f)$

Backward scattering coefficient. The coefficient which relates to backward scatterance.

    Symbol: b_b

    Unit: m^{-1}

    Relation: $b_b = 2\pi \int_{\frac{1}{2}\pi}^\pi \beta(\theta) \sin\theta \, d\theta$

    For homogeneous medium: $b_b r = -ln(1-B_b)$

(Total) attenuation coefficient. The internal attenuance of an infinitesimally thin layer

of the medium normal to the beam, divided by the thickness (Δr) of the layer.

Symbol: c

Unit: m^{-1}

Relation: $c = -\Delta C/\Delta r = -\Delta F/F \, \Delta r$

$c = a+b$

For homogeneous medium: $cr = -ln(1-C)$

Refractive index. The phase velocity of radiant energy in free space divided by the phase velocity of the same energy in a specified medium.

It is equal to the ratio of the sine of the angle of incidence (in vacuo) to the sine of the angle of refraction.

Symbol: n

Relation: $n = \sin i/\sin j$

Optical length. The geometrical length of a path multiplied with the total attenuation coefficient associated with the path.

Symbol: τ

Relation: $\tau = cr$

Degree of polarization. If a polarized radiance meter with retardation plate removed is directed to accept the beam, the polarizer rotated 180° and maximum and minimum radiances recorded, then the degree of polarization is the ratio of the difference between maximum and minimum radiances to the sum of them, i.e., the ratio of the polarized fraction to the total energy.

Symbol: p

Relation: $p = (L_{max}-L_{min})/(L_{max}+L_{min})$

Asymptotic radiance distribution. The radiance distribution which is the limit of the distribution in the hydrosphere as the depth increases infinitely. It is symmetrical around the vertical and independent of sun zenith distance.

Instruments

Diffuser. A device used to alter the angular distribution of the radiant flux from a source and depending essentially on the phenomenon of diffusion.

Collector. A device required to fulfil the definition of the quantity being measured, for instance, a Gershun tube in radiance measurements or a cosine collector in irradiance measurements.

Cosine collector. A collector which accepts radiant flux in accordance with the cosine law.

Optical filter. A device which changes, by absorption or interference, the magnitude or the spectral distribution of the radiant energy passing through it.

Neutral filter. An optical filter which reduces the magnitude of the radiant energy without changing its relative spectral distribution.

Selective or coloured filter. An optical filter which changes, by absorption, the spectral distribution of the energy passing through it.

Interference filter. An optical filter which transmits, at normal incidence, only a narrow band of wavelengths, other wavelengths being suppressed by the destructive interference of waves transmitted directly through the filter and those reflected $2n$ times, where n is an integer (from back and front faces of the filter.)

Photoconductive cell. A photocell whose electrical conductance changes under irradiation. A voltage supply is required in the cell circuit.

Photovoltaic cell. A photocell which sets up a potential difference between its terminals when exposed to radiant energy. It is a selfcontained current and voltage generator.
    Note: Term "barrier-layer" cell is deprecated.

Photoemissive cell. A photocell whose working depends upon the photoemissive effect, i.e., the capacity of certain surfaces to release electrons under the influence of radiant energy.

Photo-multiplier cell. A tube (valve) in which secondary emission multiplication is used to increase the output for a given incident radiant energy.

Irradiance meter. A radiant flux meter with plane (usually circular) cosine collecting surface (usually an opal glass) of effective area A. If F is the radiant flux recorded by the meter, then the associated irradiance is by definition $E = F/A$.

Spherical irradiance meter. A radiant flux meter with spherical collecting surface of effective area A, every elemental area of which is a cosine collector. If F is the radiant flux recorded by the meter, then the associated spherical irradiance is $E_s = F/A$.

Radiance meter. An irradiance meter which collects radiant energy from a set of directions and which has its field of view limited to a circular solid angle of Ω magnitude (defined, for example, by a cylindrical tube) whose axis is fixed normal to the plane of the collecting area of the meter. If E is the reading of the meter, the associated radiance is $L = E/\Omega$.

(Beam) attenuance meter or (beam) transmittance meter. A radiance meter which measures the beam transmittance, T, of a fixed path. The beam attenuance $C = 1 - T$.

Scatterance meter. An assembly of a collimated light source and a radiance meter which directly measures the scatterance values of an optical medium. Scatterance meters fall into three main classes: Free-angle, fixed-angle and integrating scatterance meters. The first type is designed to determine in principle all values of the volume scattering function at a given point, the second is designed to determine the function for a fixed angle, and the third type is designed to integrate directly the function over all angles so as to record the total scattering coefficient.

Some relations

PREISENDORFER (1961) has pointed out the desirability of a division of optical properties of the sea into two mutually exclusive classes, consisting of *inherent* properties and *apparent* properties. An inherent property is one that is independent of changes of the radiance distribution; an apparent property is one for which this is not the case. The inherent optical properties are the coefficients of attenuation, absorption and scattering, as well as the volume scattering function; apparent properties are, for instance, the coefficients of radiance attenuation and irradiance attenuation. Subsequent chapters will demonstrate the utility of the apparent properties in experimental studies of the underwater field, and will also formulate relationships among the various properties.

Some features in the relationship between radiance and irradiance will now be discussed. We begin by observing that the definition of radiance does not bring out its dual nature. This may be interpreted as follows (GERSHUN, 1939).

Consider a surface element ds_1 at O which emits energy in the direction θ_1 (Fig.2) and another element ds_2 at P which receives the emitted energy from the direction θ_2. The two surface elements are assumed to be small compared with the distance r between them. The intensity dI in the direction θ_1 is defined by:

$$dI = \frac{d^2 F}{d\omega_1}$$

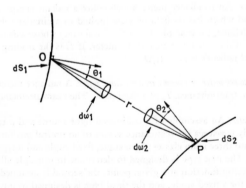

Fig.2. Diagram accompanying the definition of radiance. (After GERSHUN, 1939.)

Since the solid angle $d\omega_1$ is given by:

$$d\omega_1 = \frac{ds_2 \cos \theta_2}{r^2}$$

the irradiance dE at P must be:

$$dE = \frac{d^2 F}{ds_2} = \frac{dI \cos \theta_2}{r^2} \qquad (1)$$

This formula embodies the well-known inverse-square law and the cosine law of irradiance.

The radiance L for the outgoing field is by definition:

$$L = \frac{d^2 F}{ds_1 \cos \theta_1 d\omega_1} = \frac{dI}{ds_1 \cos \theta_1}$$

or:

$$L = \frac{d^2 F \, r^2}{ds_1 ds_2 \cos \theta_1 \cos \theta_2}$$

The same expression is found for the incoming field. The symmetry of the equation:

$$d^2 F = \frac{L ds_1 ds_2 \cos \theta_1 \cos \theta_2}{r^2} \qquad (2)$$

requires that the radiance for the outgoing field be equivalent to that for the incoming field. From eq.1 and 2 the irradiance at P may be written in the form:

$$dE = \frac{d^2 F}{ds_2} = L \cos \theta_2 d\omega_2 \qquad (3)$$

A case of special interest is the irradiance on a plane surface receiving energy from a hemisphere of constant radiance. Considering that:

$$d\omega_2 = 2\pi \sin \theta_2 d\theta_2 \qquad (4)$$

we obtain from eq.3:

$$dE = L \cos \theta_2 \cdot 2\pi \sin \theta_2 d\theta_2$$

and:

$$E = 2\pi L \int_0^{\frac{1}{2}\pi} \sin \theta_2 \cos \theta_2 d\theta_2 \qquad (5)$$

$$E = \pi L$$

Therefore a cosine diffuser, i.e., a Lambert diffuser, emits in all directions the same radiance:

$$L = \frac{E}{\pi} \tag{6}$$

PART I

Inherent Optical Properties of Sea Water

CHAPTER 2

SCATTERING

THE SCATTERING PROBLEM

Scattering, together with absorption, is the fundamental process which determines the propagation of light in sea water. One may visualize scattering simply as the deviation of light from rectilinear propagation. The scattering process leads to a change in the distribution of light which has far-reaching consequences. The significant factor in scattering studies is the volume-scattering function, which represents scatterance as a function of the scattering angle.

The theoretical and experimental investigation of the scattering problem associated with a marine environment presents considerable difficulties. One reason is that scattering in sea water has two entirely different components, namely the scattering produced by the water itself and that produced by suspended particles. The scattering by pure water shows relatively small variations, effected only by changes in temperature and pressure, whereas the particle scattering is dependent on the highly variable concentration of particulate matter. Sea water should be looked upon as a polydisperse assembly of randomly oriented irregular particles which are capable of absorption. The treatment of particle scattering cannot avoid the complexity of taking particle absorption into account.

SCATTERANCE METERS

Different types of meters

The scattering quantities have exact mathematical definitions which dictate the design of the meters to be used. In principle, measurements of scatterance involve irradiation of a sample volume by a beam of light and recording of the light scattered by the volume through various angles. Thus the basic parts of a scatterance meter are a light source, giving a beam preferable with a low divergence, and a detector, generally a photomultiplier tube. The scattering volume is defined by the intersection of the light beam with the detectivity beam.

Several types of scatterance meters have been developed. In routine work a *fixed angle* is useful; this is chosen at 45° (KALLE, 1939a; JERLOV, 1953a), or at 30° if particle concentrations are studied, and at 90° (IVANOFF, 1959) with a view to observing polarization also. *Free-angle* instruments yield values of the volume scattering function, β; the geometry of these meters generally imposes limitations on their angular range. Finally, *integrating* meters have been designed which directly record the total scattering coefficient, b. Another ground of subdivision is to distinguish laboratory meters and in situ meters.

Laboratory meters

There are on the market laboratory scatterance meters with high resolving power which apparently admit of rapid measurements of the volume scattering function. However, the meters require adaptation to the special study of ocean water. Because the latter has a low scatterance, produced by a relatively small number of particles, the beam should be chosen fairly wide; this, on the other hand, makes small angles inaccessible. A more satisfactory way is to smooth the signal from the detector. Since stray light is a crucial factor, it is also expedient to place the scattering cell in water or benzene in order to reduce the disturbing reflexions at its exterior walls.

The question arises whether water samples drawn from a water bottle and transferred to a scattering cell are representative of the condition in the water region. Firstly, great precautions are necessary to avoid contamination of the sample (JERLOV, 1953a). The water bottle should be coated with ceresin or teflon. It is obligatory to agitate the sample in the water bottle and in the scattering cell in order to secure a homogeneous sample and prevent settling of large or heavy particles. By turning the (round) cell (JERLOV, 1953a) or by using a teflon covered stirring bar (SPIELHAUS, 1965), sufficient agitation is obtained. IVANOFF (1960a) collects the samples in special glass water bottles which are placed directly in the meter and turned by means of a motor.

Considering the rapid disintegration of living cells in a sample, an immediate processing is desirable. On the other hand, heating of the sample may occur during the tests; this often leads to formation of oxygen bubbles, which multiplies the scattering of the sample. When using a pumping system instead of collection with water bottles, several of the mentioned disadvantages are avoided but a major difficulty arises due to the formation of bubbles. To avoid this effect it is necessary to work with positive pressure. SPIELHAUS (1965) has discussed the errors in the in vitro method. Inexplicably large standard errors indicate that it is impossible to assess the effect of withdrawing the sample from its environment. IVANOFF et al. (1961) have stated that the laboratory method, if employed with the utmost care, yields consistent results but that the in situ method is highly preferable.

In situ meters

In accordance with this preference, two in situ free-angle meters are selected to represent the family of scatterance instruments. In TYLER and RICHARDSON's (1958) meter (20—170°) (Fig.3) the optical system has the advantage that the limiting rays of the beam are parallel to the axis of the system and are perpendicular to the glass window of the watertight enclosure; they will thus not be deviated by the window. The scattering volume is made independent of the angle θ by the operation of a Waldram stop.

Another in situ meter (10—165°) is designed with a view to reduc-

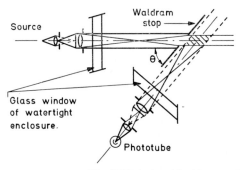

Fig.3. In situ scatterance meter (20—170°) designed by TYLER and RICHARDSON (1958).

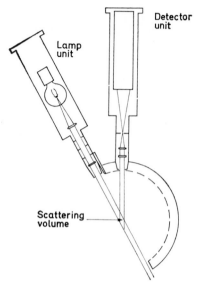

Detector
unit

Lamp
unit

Scattering
volume

Fig.4. In situ scatterance meter (10 – 165°) used by JERLOV (1961).

ing the disturbing effect of natural light (Fig.4). When released, the lamp unit falls slowly down — checked by a paddlewheel revolving in the water — and rotates around the centre of the scattering volume element. The rotation brings twelve successive stops in front of the photomultiplier tube. The width of these stops is proportional to sin θ, so that the measured scattering emanates from a constant volume.

Great interest is focussed on scatterance at small angles, which makes up a considerable part of the total scatterance. These measurements are technically the most intricate and require a meter with high resolution. A unique meter has been devised by DUNTLEY (1963) (Fig.5). His instrument employs a highly collimated beam in connection with an external central stop, so that a thin-walled hollow cylinder of light is formed (cross-hatched in Fig.5). Only light scattered by the water in this cylinder is collected through an evaluated angle of $0°.47 \pm 0°.15$.

By means of a laser and a system of mirrors, G. KULLENBERG (1966) has contrived to isolate scattering through a small angular interval defined by the half-angle of the cone of the entrance mirror (Fig.5).

Several such mirrors can be used to cover angles between 1°5 and 5°.

A third alternative for measuring small angle scatterance is to employ the in situ photographic method employed by BAUER and IVANOFF (1965). This allows records through 1°5–14° with the excellent resolution of 15′ on an average. A sketch of the meter is given in Fig.5. BAUER and MOREL (1967) have presented a firm theoretical and experimental basis for the standardization of this meter.

Integrating meter

The best adaptation to routine observation in the sea is displayed by the integrating meter designed after the principle introduced by BEUTELL and BREWER (1949); JERLOV (1961); TYLER and HOWERTON (1962). A small light source S, consisting of a lamp and an opalglass

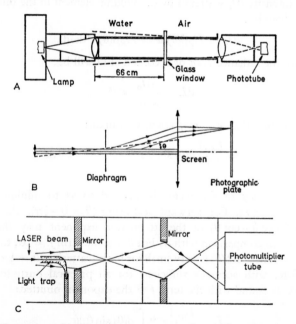

Fig.5. Three types of in situ scatterance meters for small angles. A. For 0.5° angle (DUNTLEY, 1963). B. For angles between 1.5° and 14° (BAUER and IVANOFF, 1965). C. For several defined angles between 1.5° and 5° (G. KULLENBERG, 1966).

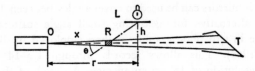

Fig.6. Integrating scatterance meter according to the principle of BEUTELL and BREWER (1949).

of surface area A, is assumed to be a cosine emitter of radiance L_0 (Fig.6). A radiance detector is placed at O with its axis parallel to the surface of S and facing a light trap T. With due regard to the attenuation by the water, the irradiance E_R on the volume element $d\nu$ at R is found from eq.2 to be:

$$E_R = \frac{L_0 A \sin^3 \theta}{h^2} e^{-ch \, \mathrm{cosec} \, \theta}$$

The intensity dI_0 scattered by the volume element in the direction RO is given by:

$$dI_0 = E_R \beta(\theta) d\nu = E_R \beta(\theta) x^2 d\omega \, dx$$

Hence the radiance L of $d\nu$ recorded at O will be:

$$dL = \frac{dI_0}{x^2 \, d\omega} e^{-cx}$$

Considering that $x = r - h \cot \theta$, we obtain:

$$dL = \frac{L_0 A}{h} \beta(\theta) \sin \theta \, e^{-cr - ch(\mathrm{cosec} \, \theta - \cot \theta)} \, d\theta$$

The geometry of the meter is adapted so as to minimize the distance $h(h \ll r)$. For forward scattering ($\theta = 0 - \frac{1}{2}\pi$), the term $f = ch (\mathrm{cosec} \, \theta - \cot \theta)$ of the attenuation exponent may then be neglected in comparison with cr. For $\theta = \pi$ the term $f = \infty$; furthermore, the function $\beta(\theta)$ is very small for back-scattering ($\theta = \frac{1}{2}\pi$ to π). Therefore, with accuracy sufficient for all practical purposes, the radiance is found with the term f of the exponent omitted:

$$L = \frac{L_0 A}{h} e^{-cr} \int_0^\pi \beta(\theta) \sin \theta \, d\theta$$

Introducing the total scattering coefficient:

$$b = 2\pi \int_0^\pi \beta(\theta) \sin \theta \, d\theta$$

we obtain:

$$b = \frac{2\pi L b}{A L_0} e^{cr}$$

TYLER and HOWERTON (1962) have suggested that for high resolving power together with maximal flux one should use a cylindrical slit source which completely surrounds the beam of detectivity and is concentric with it. It is also advisable to restrict the detectivity beam as shown in Fig.3.

The function of in situ scatterance meters may be affected by ambient natural light in the upper strata of the ocean. It is difficult to combine effective screening from natural light with free water circulation through the scattering centre. A "chopped" light source together with a suitable recorder–amplifier avoids disturbance from natural light (RICHARDSON and SHONTING, 1957). A red filter in front of the detector helps to reduce this effect. An original record of the total scattering coefficient for red light as a function of depth is depicted in Fig.7.

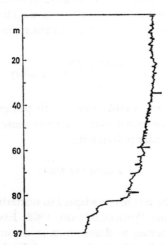

Fig.7. Original record of the total scattering coefficient for red light as a function of depth in the Sargasso Sea.

It is requisite for the whole body of optical problems to know the scattering coefficients in absolute units. A great deal of effort has been expended in calibrating procedures. In particular, TYLER (1963a) and TYLER and AUSTIN (1964) have endeavoured to lay a firm theoretical basis for the scatterance meter and to extend the theoretical analogies by PRITCHARD and ELLIOT (1960) for application to scattering by ocean water. This cannot be discussed in detail here.

SCATTERING BY WATER

Rayleigh theory

Scattering by pure water is often considered as a problem of molecular scattering. An introduction into this domain is provided by the Rayleigh equation (RAYLEIGH, 1871). A homogeneous electrical field E induces in a particle a dipole the strength, p, of which is given by:

$$p = \alpha E$$

where α is the polarizability of the particle.

The oscillating dipole radiates in all directions. For the case of N particles which are small relative to the wavelength, isotropic and distributed at random, the radiant intensity in the direction θ is given by:

$$i = \frac{8\pi^4 N \alpha^2 E^2}{\lambda^4} (1 + \cos^2 \theta)$$

which brings out the well-known fourth power law of the wavelength. It should be noted that in a strict sense only spherical top molecules have a scalar polarizability.

Fluctuation theory

An approach which is better adapted to scattering by liquids is that of fluctuation theory (SMOLUCHOWSKI, 1908; EINSTEIN, 1910). This attributes the scattering to fluctuations in density or concentration which occur in small volume elements of the fluid independent of fluctuations in neighbouring volume elements.

If i_o is the intensity of a beam of unpolarized light, the scattered intensity i is found from:

$$\frac{i}{i_o} = \frac{\pi^2}{18} \frac{\eta kT}{\lambda^4} (n^2-1)^2(n^2+2)^2(1+\cos^2\theta)$$

where η = thermal compressibility, k = Boltzmann's constant, n = refractive index and T = absolute temperature. The equation also establishes the dependence of scattering on temperature and pressure.

This formula is valid for isotropic scattering centres. If the existing anisotropy which gives rise to depolarization of the scattered light (see p. 44) is taken into account, the complete equation becomes:

$$\frac{i}{i_o} = \frac{\pi^2}{18} \frac{\eta kT}{\lambda^4} (n^2-1)^2(n^2+2)^2 \frac{6(1+\delta)}{6-7\delta} \left(1 + \frac{1-\delta}{1+\delta} \cos^2\theta\right) \quad (7)$$

By applying another relation for the change of the refractive index with pressure than that assumed by Einstein, it is possible in different ways to arrive at an alternative formula given by Vessot-King:

$$\frac{i}{i_o} = \frac{\pi^2}{2} \frac{\eta kT}{\lambda^4} (n^2-1)^2 \frac{6(1+\delta)}{6-7\delta} \left(1 + \frac{1-\delta}{1+\delta} \cos^2\theta\right) \quad (8)$$

PEYROT (1938) has finally proved that eq.8 conforms much better to experimental values for water than does eq.7. The dispersions of

TABLE I

THEORETICAL SCATTERING FUNCTION FOR PURE WATER

(After LE GRAND, 1939)

Scattering angle θ (°)	Scattering function $\beta(\theta)$ 460 nm
0—180	$3.17 \cdot 10^{-4}$
10—170	$3.13 \cdot 10^{-4}$
20—160	$3.00 \cdot 10^{-4}$
30—150	$2.80 \cdot 10^{-4}$
45—135	$2.45 \cdot 10^{-4}$
60—120	$2.11 \cdot 10^{-4}$
75—105	$1.86 \cdot 10^{-4}$
90	$1.74 \cdot 10^{-4}$

the scattering function for 90°, $\beta_o(90)$, and of the total scattering coefficient, b_o, are therefore represented by theoretical data computed by LE GRAND (1939) on the basis of eq.8 (Table I and XI).

Measurements

Many workers — the first of them, RAMAN (1922) — testify to the difficulty of preparing optically pure water. Small traces of particulate contaminations augment the scatterance drastically, especially at small angles. The possibility of obtaining accurate results is dictated chiefly by one's success in preparing pure water.

In the light of findings by DAWSON and HULBURT (1937), and by MOREL (1966), it is manifestly clear that the scattering by pure water obeys the Rayleigh λ^{-4} law. Morel has given an account of all phases of pure water scattering. His careful measurements of the scattering function in the interval 30°—150° on water distilled three times in vacuum without boiling indicate that experimental and theoretical values accord well; the observed value of $\beta_o(90)$ of 0.085 (546 nm) compares with the theoretical of 0.088. The scattering due to the various solutes present in pure sea water is difficult to observe, since sea water can be purified only by filtering. Morel has ascertained that the scatterance produced by the sea salts is minute, which is in accordance with the theoretical interpretation of HISHIDA (1953).

REFRACTIVE INDEX AND DISPERSION OF SEA WATER

The refractive index enters the formulas for scattering by sea water. The question arises as to what degree the index is influenced by changes in temperature and salinity of the water. BEIN (1935) has treated this problem exhaustively (Table II). It is evident that the dependence of the index on salinity is more marked than the dependence on temperature; neither effect is of great consequence, however.

The dispersion of refraction is more important. LAUSCHER (1955) has selected accurate refractive index data as a function of the wavelength (Table III). Although the dispersion amounts to only 4 % over the actual spectral range, it must be accounted for in the scattering computations, e.g., by means of eq.8.

It may be gathered, however, that for all practical purposes the

TABLE II

THE REFRACTION DIFFERENCE $(n_s - n_w) \cdot 10^6$ AS A FUNCTION OF TEMPERATURE AND
SALINITY FOR 587.6 NM (BEIN, 1935). THE REFRACTIVE INDEX FOR SEA WATER IS
n_s AND THAT FOR AIR SATURATED DISTILLED WATER n_w

Salinity	Temperature			
(⁰/₀₀)	0°	10°	20°	30°
20	4001	3814	3697	3621
25	4989	4759	4617	4524
30	5977	5708	5538	5429
35	6966	6657	6463	6337

mentioned effects can be neglected and a value for the refractive index
of $n = \frac{4}{3}$ adopted.

PARTICLE SCATTERING

Nature and composition of particulate material

A basic examination of the particulate matter in the sea distin-
guishes two main classes: organic and inorganic matter. Large
quantities of inorganic material are brought to the ocean by land
drainage and by winds. The organic substances are present in variable
proportions as demonstrated in Table IV. PARSONS (1963) gives the
following average relative figures to illustrate the role of the living

TABLE III

DISPERSION OF REFRACTION FOR SEA WATER $(t = 20°)$

(After LAUSCHER, 1955)

Wavelength (nm)	Refractive index	Wavelength (nm)	Refractive index
250	1.3773	486	1.3371
308	1.3569	589	1.3330
359	1.3480	768	1.3289
400	1.3433	1000	1.3247
434	1.3403	1250	1.3210

TABLE IV

DISTRIBUTION OF ORGANIC AND INORGANIC FRACTIONS IN SUSPENDED PARTICULATE
MATTER

(After PARSONS, 1963)

Region	Total suspended matter (mg/l)	% organic matter	Reference
Offshore, Pacific	10.5	62	Fox et al. (1953)[1]
Offshore, Pacific	3.8	29	
North Sea	6.0	27	Postma (1954)[1]
Wadden Sea	18.0	14	
Oceanic average	0.8—2.5	20—60*	Lisitsyn (1959)[1]
Indian Ocean	–	6—36*	
Long Island Sound	2—7	20—45	Riley (1959)[1]

* Determined from carbon $\times 2 =$ dry organic matter.
[1] Referred to in: PARSONS (1963).

component: soluble organic 100; particulate detritus 10; phytoplankton 2; zooplankton 0.2; fish 0.002. The organic detritus is to
a large extent composed of remnants of disintegrated phytoplankton
cells and of exoskeletons of zooplankton. Soluble decay products
and soluble components such as $CaCO_3$ and SiO_2 participate in the
general chain of biological transport. It has been observed that the
formation of organic detritus from soluble organic matter takes place
in the sea by flocculation (JERLOV, 1955a; Chapter 3, p.55) and
by adsorption processes (SUTCLIFFE et al., 1963).

The total particle concentration is generally studied by gravimetric
determinations (LISITSYN, 1961). Microscopic examination furnishes
information about the size distribution of the particles. For coastal
waters, JERLOV (1955b) and PICKARD and GIOVANDO (1960) found
geometric mean diameters of 16 μ and 6—17 μ, respectively. Photographic studies from an underwater chamber indicate the presence
of many large scatterers, mostly above 1 mm (NISHIZAWA et al., 1954)
(Fig.8). Direct observation reveals that fairly large detrital aggregates
are formed in the sea, to which living cells are added. INOUE et al.
(1955) stress that these delicate structures disintegrate during the
process of water sampling. The research by KREY (1961) also gives

Fig.8. Large scatterers (two specimens of *Sagitta*) seen at 10 m depth from the "Kuroshio" diving chamber. (Photo from N. Inoue and M. Kajihara.)

evidence of relatively large-sized detritus. The intricate work of establishing particle sizes in ocean water has been accomplished by LISITSYN (1961) and OCHAKOVSKY (1966a). These results, presented in Table V argue in favour of dominant cross-sections (eq.15) being above 2 μ in diameter.

TABLE V

SIZE DISTRIBUTION OF PARTICLES IN THE SEA

Size distribution of particles (% total particle number) in the sea (LISITSYN, 1961)

Region	Depth (m)	Concentration (mg/l)	Fractions μ					
			>100	100—50	50—10	10—5	5—1	<1
West Pacific	5—7	0.279	0.33	–	11.67	1.81	2.89	83.23
	100	0.800	0.20	0.20	2.80	3.09	2.83	90.86

Size distribution of particles (relative number) in the sea (OCHAKOVSKY, 1966a)

Region	b m⁻¹	Fractions μ					
		>50	50—25	25—10	10—5	5—2.5	2.5—1
Mediterranean	0.10	3.5	10.4	40.7	23.6	56.5	480
	0.15	2.8	14.3	56.1	31.5	81.0	326
	0.20	1.8	10.3	41.4	28.3	57.5	890

Geometric optics

The scattering process may be treated on a purely theoretical basis as a forward solution of Maxwell's equations. However, a short discussion within the framework of classical large particle optics will facilitate our understanding of the concept of scattering. Scattering may be looked upon as the result of three physical phenomena:

(*1*) Through the action of the particle, light is deviated from rectilinear propagation (diffraction).

(*2*) Light penetrates the particle and emerges with or without one or more internal reflections (refraction).

(*3*) Light is reflected externally.

It is a matter of some significance that diffraction is independent of the composition of the particle, whereas refraction and reflection are determined by the refractive index of the particle.

Particle size is the major parameter in scattering. The influence of shape from the point of view of geometric optics has been discussed in a conclusive way by HODKINSON (1963). In the case of irregular, nonabsorbing, randomly-oriented particles, the diffraction pattern should be similar to that produced by spherical particles with the same projected area. There will also be little change in the external reflections, since the probability of reflection for all angles of incidence will be equal. The first refraction by irregular particles will also be similar to that for spheres, whereas the second refraction may show appreciable angular deviations. It follows that opaque irregular particles, for which refraction is negligible, behave in the same way as opaque spheres.

Mie theory

MIE (1908) has employed electromagnetic theory to derive a rigorous expression for the perturbation of a plane monochromatic wave by spherical nonabsorbing particles. The Mie theory is difficult to comprehend in simple terms. The basic equations are introduced here in order to give an idea of the general reasoning which is utilized.

The treatment of a monodisperse system of particles of given refractive index is based on the assumption that the scattered light has the same wavelength as the incident light and that the particles are independent in the sense defined by VAN DE HULST (1957).

Independence requires that the distance between the spheres is at least three times their radii and has the consequence that the intensities scattered by the individual particles can be added. Another limitation is that the particles are assumed to be irradiated only by the original beam, i.e., no multiple scattering occurs. Hence total scatterance is proportional to the number of particles.

The quantity i_1 is defined as the intensity scattered in the direction θ by a single isotropic sphere from an incident polarized beam of unit intensity whose electric vector is perpendicular to the plane of observation (i.e., the plane containing the direction of propagation of the incident wave and the direction of observation). Similarly, the quantity i_2 refers to the electric vector in the plane of observation. The Mie theory furnishes these quantities:

$$i_1 = \left| \sum_{n=1}^{\infty} \left\{ A_n \frac{dP_n(x)}{dx} + B_n \left| x \frac{dP_n(x)}{dx} - (1-x^2) \frac{d^2 P_n(x)}{dx^2} \right| \right\} \right|^2$$

$$i_2 = \left| \sum_{n=1}^{\infty} \left\{ A_n \left| x \frac{dP_n(x)}{dx} - (1-x^2) \frac{d^2 P_n(x)}{dx^2} \right| + B_n \frac{dP_n(x)}{dx} \right\} \right|^2$$

$$(9)$$

with $x = -\cos \theta$; and $P_n(x) =$ Legendre polynomial of order n.

The functions A_n and B_n involve the Riccati–Bessel and Riccati–Hankel functions, and are related to the Bessel functions of half-integral order. The only physical parameters which enter into these functions are:

$$\alpha = \pi D/\lambda$$
$$\beta = m\alpha$$

$$(10)$$

where $D =$ diameter of the particle; $\lambda =$ wavelength of the incident wave in the surrounding medium, and $m =$ refractive index of the particle relative to the surrounding medium.

The quantity scattered in the direction θ from a randomly polarized beam of unit intensity will be:

$$i(\theta) = \frac{\lambda^2}{8\pi^2} (i_1 + i_2)$$

On integrating $i(\theta)$ with respect to θ, we obtain the total scattered radiation:

$$I = 2\pi \int_0^{\pi} i(\theta) \sin \theta \, d\theta = \frac{\lambda^2}{4\pi} \int_0^{\pi} (i_1 + i_2) \sin \theta \, d\theta \qquad (11)$$

If this integral is divided by the cross-sectional area $\pi D^2/4$ of the particle, a dimensionless quantity K is obtained:

$$\frac{4I}{\pi D^2} = K = \frac{1}{\alpha^2} \int_0^\pi (i_1 + i_2) \sin \theta \, d\theta \tag{12}$$

Eq.9 and 12 yield the following result:

$$K = \frac{2}{\alpha^2} \sum_{n=1}^\infty \frac{n^2(n+1)^2}{2n+1} (|A_n|^2 + |B_n|^2) \tag{13}$$

The quantity K is called the efficiency factor, or the effective area coefficient. It follows from the definition of the scattering coefficient b that with N particles per unit volume we have:

$$b = KN\pi D^2/4 \tag{14}$$

For the case of a polydispersed system, the scattering coefficient is given by:

$$b = \frac{\pi}{4} \sum_{i=1}^n K_i N_i D_i^2 \tag{15}$$

The results of the Mie theory are obtained as a series which converges rather slowly for particles as large as several wavelengths in diameter. However, this does not present any serious problem for modern electronic computers.

Enlarging the treatment to encompass absorbing particles requires the introduction of a complex refractive index:

$$m = n - in' \tag{16}$$

where $n' = a\lambda/4\pi$, a being, as usual, the absorption coefficient. The steps of computation in this case are described by VAN DE HULST (1957).

Application of the Mie theory to sea water

Sea water is a dilute suspension of independent particles of various sizes, shapes and compositions. Multiple scattering may be disregarded for the usually small volumes which are studied in scatterance meters. Before a broad theoretical treatment of scattering by sea water can be contemplated, a great deal of observational effort

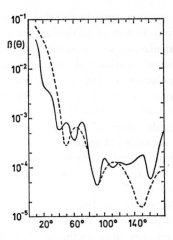

Fig.9. Scattering functions computed from the Mie theory for nonabsorbing spheres with $m = 1.20$ and $\alpha = \pi D/\lambda = 30$ (continuous line) (after ASHLEY and COBB, 1958), and with $m = 1.15$ and $\alpha = 5$ (dashed line). (After PANGONIS and HELLER, 1960.)

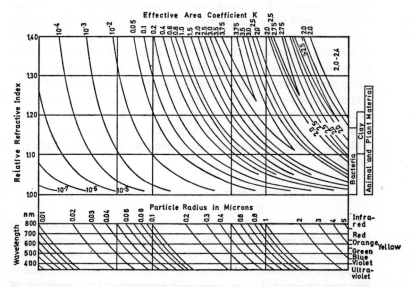

Fig.10. Particle scattering diagram computed on the basis of Rayleigh's equation and the Mie theory for nonabsorbing spheres. (After BURT, 1956.)

is still required to increase one's knowledge about the size distribution and the absorption effect of particulate matter.

Nevertheless, calculations for monodisperse systems are relevant to any consideration of experimental scattering data from the marine environment. Calculations of the volume scattering function for nonabsorbing spheres are shown in Fig.9. The two curves exhibit the oscillatory trend which is typical for monodisperse suspension. If particles of a wide range of sizes are present, the fluctuating features would be virtually obliterated.

It is a conspicuous trend in such curves that with increasing particle size the forward scattering is intensified and that a slight minimum is formed at 90°, indicating that scatterance through this angle is less than backscatter at 180°.

BURT (1956) has presented a useful scattering diagram (Fig.10) which shows the effective area coefficient K as a function of size, wavelength and relative refractive index. His computations are based on Rayleigh's law and the Mie theory for nonabsorbing spheres. The diagram covers a radius range $0.01-5\ \mu$ and an index range $1.02-1.40$, including indices for particulate material present in natural waters. With increasing particle radius the coefficient increases rapidly at small radii, then it passes a maximum for sizes of the same order as the wavelength $(K > 3.0)$ and tends — after some fluctuations — towards a constant value of 2.0 for large sizes irrespective of the wavelength. It may seem anomalous that a large particle scatters twice the amount of light it can intercept by its geometric cross-section. This is, however, a well-known diffractive phenomenon. A circular opaque disc observed at a *great* distance also diffracts around its edges, and into a narrow solid angle, a quantity of light which is exactly the same as that intercepted by the disc (Babinets principle).

Observed values of the effective area coefficient

The Mie theory is well confirmed for scatterers having geometrical forms simple enough to be mathematically tractable. Some experimental data on water suspensions are contained in the following references. HODKINSON (1963) studied size-graded fractions of quartz, flint and diamond dust in water and demonstrated the approach of the K factor to a numerical value of 2. JERLOV and KULLENBERG

TABLE VI

EFFICIENCY FACTOR FOR VARIOUS SUSPENSIONS

Suspension	μ	K
minerogenic	1	1.4
	3	2.2
	7	2.4
	9	2.2
	12	2.3
calcareous	10	2.7
	30	3.2

(1953) measured scatterance on uniform minerogenic suspensions. Their results (Table VI) provide evidence that the scattering coefficient is proportional to the concentration of particles or to their number and that large-particle scattering with $K = 2$ occurs for sizes above 1 μ. This is in agreement with coefficients computed by BURT (1954b). Calcite suspensions show the same features (Table VI, JERLOV, 1955b). The behaviour of some marine organisms of different relative refractive index as scattering objects is also studied by JERLOV, who concludes that particles composed of calcium carbonate or silica produce high scattering whereas minimum scattering is obtained for green algae, the chief constituent of which is cellulose. The relative refractive index of minerals in the sea has been estimated by PAVLOV and GRECHUSHNIKOV (1966) to be 1.17.

THE VOLUME SCATTERING FUNCTION

Observations

A body of experimental data on the volume scattering function β is given in Table VII, supplemented by Fig.11. These results comprise all available observations in different oceanic waters, and are obtained by means of the various types of instruments described. We distinguish between the laboratory (in vitro) method and the in situ method with a view to laying more emphasis on the latter values.

OBSERVATIONS OF THE VOLUME SCATTERING FUNCTI

			Laboratory measurements				
	(1)	(2)	(3)	(4)	(5)	(6)	
Angle θ (°)	Hulburt (1945) Chesapeake Bay	Atkins and Poole (1952) English Channel	Kozlyaninov (1957) East China Sea	Spielhaus (1965) Sargasso Sea	Ochakovsky (1966b) Mediterranean	Sasaki et al. (1962a) off Japan	
						600 m	3000
	(white light)	(blue light)	(blue light)	(546 nm)	(546 nm)	(576 nm)	(576 n
1			7,200		10,000		
1.5							
3							
5			1,100		830		
7							
10	247	232	312		230		
20	61	62	62		57	39	30
30	22	18	22	22	12	22	14
45	8.5	6.0	6.9	6.0	7.7	5.5	3.8
60	3.0	2.5	3.1	2.7	4.6	2.9	1.8
75	1.4	1.5	1.8	1.6	2.3	1.2	1.8
90	1.0	1.0	1.0	1.0	1.0	1.0	1.0
105	1.0	0.82	0.49	1.0	0.9	0.8	1.1
120	1.2	0.67	0.44	0.9	0.8	0.7	1.0
135	1.5	0.90	0.50	1.0	0.8	1.0	1.4
150	2.2				0.9	1.2	1.8
165	3.1						
180							

* Normalized.

Shape of the scattering function

The β-curves exhibit the distinctive properties of a polydispersed system, being smoothed in contrast to the oscillatory curve for a monodisperse system. The most striking feature in the curve shape is the pronounced forward scattering. DUNTLEY (1963) suggests that the magnitude of the β-function may merge tangentially with that of the irradiating beam at vanishingly small angles.

...MALIZED AT 90°; SURFACE WATER EXCEPT COLUMN *6*

	In situ measurements						
angle θ (°)	(7) JERLOV (1961) east north Atlantic (465 nm)	(8) TYLER (1961a) Californian coast (522 nm)	(9) DUNTLEY (1963) Lake Winnipesakee (522 nm)	(10) BAUER and IVANOFF (1965) off Monaco (546 nm)	(11) BAUER and MOREL (1966) The Channel Mediterranean (546 nm)	(12) KULLENBERG (1966) Sargasso Sea 465 nm	640 nm
1			14,000				
1.5				100*	26,100		4,000
3				29	8,500		2,500
5			1,300	9	2,990		1,500
7				3.5	1,300		900
10	292		319	1.2	500	118	380
20	74	67	63			29	69
30	23	20	21			8.2	22
45	7.5	6.7	6.7			4.4	8.7
60	2.96	2.7	2.81			2.09	3.05
75	1.72	1.51	1.49			1.24	1.57
90	1.00	1.00	1.00			1.00	1.00
105	0.95	0.91	0.81			0.97	0.89
120	1.05	0.94	0.76			1.14	0.93
135	1.30	1.05	0.78			1.37	1.12
150	1.55	1.18	0.82			1.72	1.38
165	1.90	1.38	0.86			1.82	1.67
180		1.49					

A remarkable point in Table VII is the similarity between the forward β-functions for most surface waters. For waters poor in particles, however, the scattering by the water itself plays a greater part in the total scattering, and the β-function tends to approach the symmetrical function valid for pure water. Convincing proof of this statement is furnished by SASAKI et al. (1962a; Table VII, column *6*) and by KULLENBERG (1966; column *12*). A group of functions derived from systematic measurements (in vitro) by IVANOFF and MOREL (1964) and MOREL (1966) exhibit the change of the function from

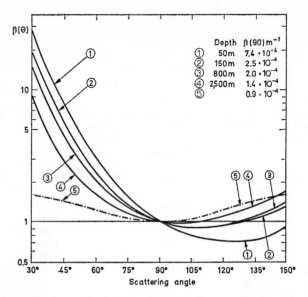

Fig.11. Family of scattering functions (30—150°) for water samples of the western Mediterranean (*1—4*) compared with the theoretical function for pure water (*5*). (After MOREL, 1966.)

surface water to clear deep water in the western Mediterranean (Fig.11). The back-scattered field forms a regular pattern in this diagram. It follows from these results that the scatterance (546 nm) by the water itself at 90°, $\beta_0(90)$, makes up 13 % of the total scatterance at 90°, $\beta(90)$, in the surface water and no less than 70 % in the deepest water. But there is in the latter case still a large span between β and β_0 at small angles.

Particle scattering

In this context we shall deal with the observed difference between total scatterance and pure water scatterance. Fig.12 is a condensation of results of different investigators, and goes to prove that total particle scattering is virtually independent of the water mass. How can this circumstance be explained in regard to the nature of the scattering process? ATKINS and POOLE (1952) suggest that the scattering within the region 20—155° is due chiefly to refraction through large transparent mineral particles, whereas refraction through organic matter may be responsible for the scattering through smaller angles. The preponderance of forward scattering is also ascribed by DUNTLEY (1963) to refraction of rays by relatively large particles of biological material that have a low relative index of refraction.

It is necessary, however, not to overlook the effect of diffraction.

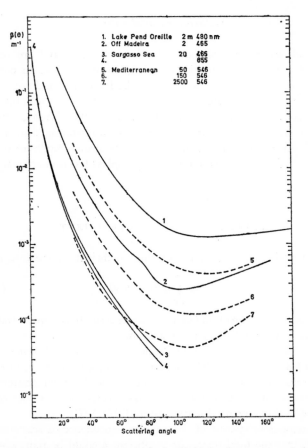

Fig.12. Particle scattering functions obtained by deducting the theoretical function for pure water from functions observed in the Mediterranean (sample *5—7*; MOREL, 1966), in the Sargasso Sea (*3, 4*; KULLENBERG, 1966), off Madeira (*2*; JERLOV, 1961), and in Lake Pend Oreille (*1*; TYLER, 1961a).

Through theoretical and experimental studies of size-graded fractions of inter alia quartz and coal dust suspended in water, HODKINSON (1963) has demonstrated that the forward scattering is diffraction dominated. Diffraction is of the same magnitude as refraction + reflection at 15° even for quartz, and at 30° for coal. The forward scattering is thus determined chiefly by the size of particles, very little by their shape and fairly little by their composition.

Scattering in coastal waters

Coastal waters are influenced by land drainage and are often supplied with large quantities of terrigeneous material. In consequence, they are likely to show less regular features than do offshore waters. It suffices to state that one group of measurements (JERLOV and FUKUDA, 1960; PICKARD and GIOVANDO, 1960; TYLER, 1961a) is characterized by more pronounced forward scattering than is the general oceanic function, whereas another group represented by HINZPETER (1962) and SPIELHAUS (1965) displays less forward scattering.

TOTAL SCATTERING COEFFICIENT

When evaluating the total scattering coefficient by the integral:

$$b = 2\pi \int_0^\pi \beta(\theta) \sin \theta \, d\theta \qquad (17)$$

the scatterance at small angles becomes crucial. It is demonstrated in Table VIII that half of the scatterance derived from column *3* in Table VII is contained within a cone of half-angle 9°. Considering the detailed procedure in determining small-angle scatterance, a more feasible way to arrive at absolute values of the total scattering coefficient would be to use an integrating meter. Some values of *b* obtained in this way are discussed later (Table XIII).

The regular behaviour of the angular dependence of scatterance suggests that the total scattering coefficient *b* could be represented by scatterance through a certain angle. JERLOV (1953a) studied the particle content in different oceans with the aid of scattering measurements through 45°, and proved by computation from available values

TABLE VIII

PERCENTAGE OF THE SCATTERING COEFFICIENT FOR DIFFERENT ANGULAR INTERVALS[1]

Angle (θ)	$b(0°-\theta°)/b(0°-180°)$ (%)	Angle (θ)	$b(0°-\theta°)/b(0°-180°)$ (%)
5°	35	45°	91
10°	55	90°	98
20°	75	180°	100
30°	85		

[1] From column 3, Table VII.

of the scattering function that a linear correlation exists between $\beta(45)$ and the total scattering coefficient b. The apparent constancy of the ratio $\beta(45)/b$ has been corroborated by TYLER (1961c) for prepared stable suspensions. The theoretical proof has been furnished by DEIRMENDJAN (1963), who computed normalized intensities of scattering by a polydispersed system and found that the quantity $(P_1+P_2)/8\pi$ (eq.9) is constant around 40° with a value of 0.1 regardless of the size distribution function.

DISPERSION OF SCATTERING

Wavelength selectivity of scattering by sea water arises from the following three agencies:

(1) Scattering by the water itself (β_0).
(2) Scattering by small-sized particles.
(3) Absorption by particles.

The highly selective (λ^{-4}) water scattering accounts for most of the selectivity stated for sea water, according to the value assigned β_0 in the total scatterance β at a given angle. This influence is important in the back-scattered field for clear waters, but practically disappears at small angles for all natural waters.

The constellation between particle scatterance, size and wavelength in Burt's diagram (Fig.10) states that spectral selectivity occurs for sizes below 1 μ. Results for the particle scattering function at different wavelengths summarized in Fig.12, on the other hand, furnish support for the notion that forward particle scattering in the ocean is virtually independent of wavelength, i.e., that the cross-section of small particles is of minor magnitude. For high angles, even at 90°, it seems that wavelength dependence appears. The size problem is further discussed in the next section.

The view that scattering of marine particles is wavelength-invariant cannot be wholly accepted in regard to the fact that scattering is associated with absorption in the particles. This brings up the theme of coloured particles in the sea, manifest, for instance, in discolourations due to abundance of organisms with specific colour

TABLE IX

DISPERSION OF THE SCATTERING FUNCTION. SURFACE WATER OFF PLYMOUTH

(After ATKINS and POOLE, 1954)

$\beta(45)$			$\beta(90)$		
Blue ($\cdot 10^{-7}$)	Green ($\cdot 10^{-7}$)	Red ($\cdot 10^{-7}$)	Blue ($\cdot 10^{-7}$)	Green ($\cdot 10^{-7}$)	Red ($\cdot 10^{-7}$)
81	71	76	19	16	17
70	48	54	16	10	10

TABLE X

SCATTERING COEFFICIENT FOR THE RED AND THE BLUE. PACIFIC STATION
($00°02'$ N $152°07'$ W)

(After JERLOV, 1953a)

Depth (m)	Scattering coefficient (km^{-1})		Depth (m)	Scattering coefficient (km^{-1})	
	blue	red		blue	red
0	54	51	394	24	24
25	57	50	492	24	27
49	45	41	590	21	23
74	51	46	787	28	28
98	44	35	984	27	30
147	25	22	1431	27	30
197	31	30	1918	19	19
295	47	43	2385	13	11

(Chapter 13, p.151). It is often found that the scatterance shows an irregular trend over the spectrum as illustrated in Table IX. Evidence of higher scatterance in the red than in the blue is given by JERLOV (1953a) (Table X). These scattering objects which looked red also by visual observation were encountered between 500 and 1,500 m in the central Pacific as a peculiar phenomenon at two stations only. For the rest it was found from thousands of observations that $\beta(45)$ is 7 % higher at 465 nm than at 625 nm; the difference accounts for the selectivity of the water itself.

SCATTERING AND PARTICLE SIZE

A large majority of investigators of the optical domain concur in the view that particle scattering in surface waters is produced chiefly by large particles ($> 2 \mu$), and is thus virtually independent of the wavelength. This is strongly supported by the results of direct microscopic examinations as presented in the section on nature and composition of particulate material. Comparisons between the particle scattering functions in Fig.12 and theoretical functions for non-absorbing spheres (Fig.9) generally indicate fairly large particles; the findings by SASAKI et al. (1962a) for deep water, however, suggest sizes of less than 1 μ.

One may well be apprehensive about attributing wavelength selectivity of scattering solely to size. It seems desirable in most cases to take account of the actual absorption of the particles – discussed in the preceding section – and to enlarge the theoretical treatment to include the case of absorbing particles (eq.16).

There is every reason to believe that particle size distributions in coastal waters are not consistent. HANAOKA et al. (1960) computed particle diameters of 2—5 μ in bay-water of Japan. From scattering measurements on water samples collected off the Po River, in conjunction with a particle settling procedure, JERLOV (1958) derived a size distribution curve peaked at 3.5 μ. On the other hand, BURT (1955) ascribed the selectivity observed in Chesapeake Bay largely to an abundance of small particles. Similar results were obtained by HINZPETER (1962) by considering the dispersion of the scattering function measured in the Baltic.

MULTIPLE SCATTERING

Multiple scattering involves the irradiation of every volume element of the water not only by the original beam but also by light scattered from all other elements, so that the light is scattered several times. The effect of multiple scattering increases with the particle concentration and with the size of the irradiated volume. HARTEL's (1940) theoretical model based on the Mie theory considers successive angular distributions for each successive order of scattering. Experimental facts match the predictions of the theory for spherical particles in high concentrations. A comprehensive review of multiple scattering is presented by WOODWARD (1964).

Owing to the small volumes and the low particle concentrations studied in scatterance meters, multiple scattering is minute and can in most cases be neglected. Nevertheless, studies on turbid media may help elucidate the scattering mechanism and thereby contribute to understanding of scattering of natural radiant energy in the sea. TIMOFEEVA (1951b, 1957) has contributed extensive laboratory investigations on concentrated suspensions, and has demonstrated the change towards isotropic scattering when absorption becomes small compared to scattering. Similar model experiments have been conducted by BLOUIN and LENOBLE (1962), who in particular applied the radiate transfer approach to their results.

POLARIZATION OF SCATTERED LIGHT

Polarization, in addition to absorption and scattering, is a manifestation of the interaction of light with matter. Properly speaking, we have to deal only with unpolarized light and elliptically polarized light. In the unpolarized state there is no preferred direction in the plane of oscillation of the electric (and the magnetic) vector. Elliptical polarization implies that the terminus of the electric vector describes an ellipse in this plane. Circular and linear polarization are special cases in which the ellipse degenerates into a circle and a line, respectively. The partially polarized light which is usually encountered in nature, is a mixture of unpolarized and polarized light.

Theory

Since polarization occurs in reflection and refraction processes at interfaces, it is not surprising to find polarization arising from the more complicated processes of scattering. The following simple reasoning may give some insight into the nature of polarization for small particles (small with respect to the wavelength) or scattering centres which produce isotropic scattering. If $I_\parallel$ and $I_\perp$ are the intensities of light scattered parallel and perpendicular to a plane through the incident and scattered beams, the total intensity of light scattered through angle θ will be:

$$I = I_\parallel + I_\perp$$

By definition, the degree of polarization p is given by:

$$p = \frac{I_\perp - I_\parallel}{I_\perp + I_\parallel}$$

Simple geometric considerations show that:

$$I_\perp = A^2 \qquad I_\parallel = A^2 \cos^2 \theta, \tag{18}$$

and thus that:

$$p = \frac{1 - \cos^2 \theta}{1 + \cos^2 \theta} = \frac{\sin^2 \theta}{1 + \cos^2 \theta} \tag{19}$$

This formula was derived by Rayleigh and can also be deduced from the Mie formula (eq.9). It provides for a symmetrical p-curve and for complete polarization at $\theta = \frac{1}{2}\pi$. The electric vector oscillates in a plane perpendicular to the plane of vision. From the above equation it also follows that:

$$I = I(\tfrac{1}{2}\pi)(1 + \cos^2 \theta) \tag{20}$$

which is valid for isotropic scattering centres.

Eq.19 and 20 are not strictly applicable to water. It is a well-known fact (RAMAN, 1922) that pure water permits only partial polarization at $\theta = \frac{1}{2}\pi$. The anisotropy of the scattering centres may be accounted for by adding to eq.18 an unpolarized intensity $2B^2$ scattered uniformly over all directions (DAWSON and HULBURT, 1941). We then have:

$$I_\perp = A^2 + B^2 \qquad I_\parallel = A^2 \cos^2 \theta + B^2$$

It is now convenient to introduce a polarization defect term δ defined by:

$$\delta = \frac{I(\frac{1}{2}\pi)_{\parallel}}{I(\frac{1}{2}\pi)_{\perp}} \tag{21}$$

This may be reexpressed as:

$$\delta = \frac{B^2}{A^2 + B^2}$$

from which it follows that:

$$p(\tfrac{1}{2}\pi) = \frac{1-\delta}{1+\delta} \tag{22}$$

The corresponding expression for the intensity may thus be written:

$$I = I(\tfrac{1}{2}\pi)\left(1 + \frac{1-\delta}{1+\delta}\cos^2\theta\right) = I(\tfrac{1}{2}\pi)[1 + p(\tfrac{1}{2}\pi)\cos^2\theta] \tag{23}$$

which is valid for pure water. Reliable measurements have determined δ to be 0.090 which yields $p(\tfrac{1}{2}\pi) = 83.5\%$.

Mie's formal solution for spheres predicts that the scattered light is generally elliptically polarized, even if the incident beam has linear polarization. For particles having linear dimensions about equal to the wavelength, the polarization curve $p(\theta)$ is not symmetrical; with increasing size it develops a disordered series of maxima and minima which have no simple interpretation. The dispersion of polarization behaves in a similar irregular way. The degree of polarization for a suspension will depend on several particle characteristics of observation besides the angle, namely: (1) composition, or rather refractive index; (2) shape; and (3) size; generally the degree of polarization is less for large particles than for small.

Measurements

Polarization of scattered light is studied principally by means of a scatterance meter provided with a polarizing prism between the scattering volume and the detector (Fig.13). IVANOFF (1959) in particular has explored the possibility of employing the scatterance $\beta(90)$ and the degree of polarization $p(90)$ as independent parameters for characterizing water masses. A diagram shown in Fig.14 (IVA-

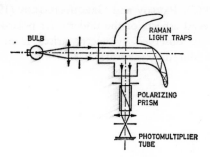

Fig.13. Principal design of laboratory polarimeter. (After IVANOFF, 1959.)

NOFF, 1961) summarizes data collected in waters off Monaco. The two limiting straight lines converge to a point characterized by $p = 88 \%$, which value thus represents pure water. If mean values are taken, a linear relationship between β and p is obtained.

TIMOFEEVA (1961) has made extensive studies of the polarization of turbid suspensions. The angular distribution of the degree of polarization does not conform to eq.19 in this case. Polarization observations in the sea, on the other hand, prove that maximum polarization occurs near 90° regardless of wavelength (Chapter 11), and that the angular distribution is best described by the symmetrical eq.19. This is supported by laboratory measurements carried out by

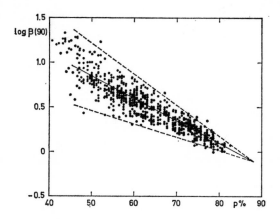

Fig.14. Relation between scatterance $\beta(90)$ and degree of polarization $p(90)$ for waters off Monaco. (After IVANOFF, 1961.)

HINZPETER (1962). PAVLOV and GRECHUSHNIKOV (1966), who have considered several aspects of the underwater polarization problem, believe that the observed symmetry arises from dominance of polarization produced by the water itself.

Elsevier's Scientific Publications

For information about new books in the following fields, please check square(s) and complete reverse of this card.

- ☐ ORGANIC CHEMISTRY
- ☐ INORGANIC CHEMISTRY
- ☐ BIOCHEMISTRY, BIOPHYSICS
- ☐ MEDICINE
- ☐ PHYSICS AND MATHEMATICS
- ☐ TECHNOLOGY, ENGINEERING
- ☐ BUILDING AND BUILDING RESEARCH
- ☐ MULTILINGUAL TECHNICAL DICTIONARIES - GLOSSARIES - LEXICA
- ☐ GEOLOGY AND GEOPHYSICS

(please print or type)

Name: ....

Address: ....

....

....

....

Elsevier's Scientific Publications

You received this card in one of our publications. It would greatly assist us in serving you further if, when returning it for more information, you would indicate below how you heard of the book or books now in your possession. We thank you for your co-operation.

☐ Bookseller's recommendation
☐ Books sent on approval by bookseller
☐ Displays in bookshops
☐ Reviews
☐ Advertisements
☐ Personal recommendation
☐ References in books and journals
☐ Publisher's catalogue
☐ Circular received from publisher
☐ Circular received from bookseller
☐ Listing in a subject catalogue of bookseller

POSTCARD

ELSEVIER PUBLISHING COMPANY

P.O. BOX 211

AMSTERDAM-W.
THE NETHERLANDS

CHAPTER 3

BEAM ATTENUATION

THE ATTENUATION PROCESS

So far we have treated scattering as a separate phenomenon. The next step is to consider the attenuation resulting from the combined action of scattering and absorption. A study which exhibits the fundamental features in the attenuation process has been reported by DUNTLEY (1963). The experiment deals with the angular distribution of radiance at different distances from a uniform, spherical, underwater lamp. The distribution curves in Fig.15 show the existence of direct image-forming light. The direct rays have not been scattered but only absorbed between the lamp and the receiver. The non-scattered or monopath irradiance E_r at normal incidence at a distance r from a lamp of intensity I is attenuated according to Allard's law:

$$E_r = I\, e^{-cr}/r^2$$

The distribution of scattered light appearing in Fig.15 brings out the pronounced forward scattering, common to natural waters. This

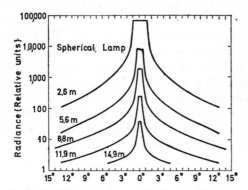

Fig.15. Angular distribution of apparent radiance for different distances from a uniform spherical lamp. (After DUNTLEY, 1963.)

is seen as a glow of light surrounding the lamp. The total light is the sum of the non-scattered (mono-path) and the scattered (multi-path) irradiance. Obviously, the latter component becomes dominant at large lamp distances.

Further aspects of the characteristic transmission process are given by REPLOGLE and STEINER (1965), who conclude that the scattered and unscattered components of light are separable. The unscattered light produces images with angular resolution at least as small as 1'.

BEAM TRANSMITTANCE METERS

Principal function

The simple principle of the beam transmittance or attenuance meter is to produce a parallel beam of light which, after passing a water path of fixed length, impinges on a detector, usually a photocell. The performance of the meter is improved by high collimation of the beam. With an optical system of the type shown in Fig.5, the divergence is minimized so as to become negligible (DUNTLEY, 1963). Obviously, a laser beam provides a perfect solution to this problem.

The beam transmittance meter is designed for the purpose of measuring attenuation coefficient, defined as absorption coefficient plus total scattering coefficient. Therefore, the meter must be highly efficient in excluding the scattered light. No meter could conform to this ideal requirement, because the detector must have a reception cone of finite magnitude. This may be critical on account of the strong scattering through small angles. The errors due to this shortcoming of the meter have been discussed by GUMPRECHT and SLIEPCEVICH (1953), WILLIAMS (1955), JONES and WILLS (1956), JERLOV (1957), PREISENDORFER (1958), and DUNTLEY (1963). In particular, Gumprecht and Sliepcevich have closely investigated the dependence of the meter's geometry on the transmittance measurements. With a lens and a diaphragm in front of the detector, the acceptance angle 2θ is defined by (Fig.16):

$$tg\,\theta = r/f$$

where r = radius of the aperture of the diaphragm and f = focal distance of the lens.

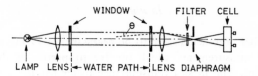

Fig. 16. Typical design of in situ beam transmittance meter. (After JOSEPH, 1949a.)

In order to assess the effect of forward scattering, we tentatively put $r = 0.9$ mm and $f = 50$ mm. The half-angle of acceptance θ is then about 1°. For ocean water, about 5 % of the total scattering occurs in the interval 0—1°. This entails a positive error of 3 % in the attenuation coefficient for blue light. It is obvious that the error can be reduced by simple means to a level which does not affect the accuracy of the results.

Laboratory meters

The precautions which should be taken with the water samples were discussed on p.16. A severe complication in most laboratory measurements arises from total reflection from the walls of the sample tubes (COOPER, 1961). The reflected light generates scattered light which enters the aperture of the detector. If the tube is long compared with its width, even direct reflected light may be recorded.

The remedy for this shortcoming would be to use baffled tubes or to place the tubes in water, in which case the scattered light virtually disappears and total reflection does not interfere.

For the measurement of low attenuance by ocean water, a long geometric light path is desirable. Attempts have been made to adapt spectrophotometers to meet this requirement. LENOBLE and SAINT-GUILLY (1955) have studied the attenuance of distilled water in the ultra-violet region by means of a spectrophotometer which can be provided with tubes of alternatively 1 m and 4 m length. BURT (1958) has modified a Beckmann DU Quartz Prism Spectrophotometer for work at sea using a 50 cm cell assembly.

Initial experiments with laser light of different wavelengths have been conducted by KNESTRICK et al. (1965). They utilized an optical path of no less than 36 m in a model basin containing filtered Potomac River water. Careful tests proved that scattered light did not contribute to the measured signals.

In situ meters

No further arguments seem to be necessary for giving preference to in situ measurements which involve properties of the natural environment. The in situ transmittance meter has for a long time been an effective means of studying the optical properties especially of coastal waters. If furnished with an adequate depth sensing unit, the instrument yields records of transmittance as a function of depth even in rough weather.

The meter depicted in Fig.16 (JOSEPH, 1949a) has served as a prototype for several later models. Various designs which differ in technical details have been described by NISHIZAVA and INOUE (1958), FUKUDA (1958), SASAKI et al. (1958b), TYLER et al. (1959), OCHA-KOVSKY (1960), and BALL and LaFOND (1964). As a rule, the entrance window of the photocell unit is made smaller than the width of the beam. Baffles mounted along the light path are used to reduce the disturbing effect of daylight. Following the original idea of PETTERS-SON (1934), some workers have utilized reflection against one or several plane mirrors in order to secure a long light path without employing an instrument of unmanageable length (WATTENBERG, 1938; RICHARDSON and SHONTING, 1957; TIMOFEEVA, 1960; NISHIZAVA and INOUE, 1964). Some improvement is achieved by introducing concave mirrors. PARAMANOV (1964) uses one concave mirror in connection with close baffling of the incident as well as of the reflected beam. An optical path of 10 m can be attained by multiple reflections between three concave mirrors of equal curvature (JERLOV, 1957).

It is expedient to employ the signal obtained with the meter in air as a standard, in particular when the beam is cylindrically limited as shown in Fig.3. The ratio of the signal for water to that for air is, within a large range, independent of the emission of the lamp. It should be observed that when submerging the meter the reflection losses at the windows are appreciably diminished. Another effect which may increase the signal is that any existing divergence of the beam in air will be reduced in water because of a predictable change of refraction at the window of the lamp unit. MATTHÄUS (1965) has designed a meter which compares in situ the attenuance of sea water to that of a standard of distilled water. This method renders any calibration of the instrument superfluous.

Finally, we should point out the usefulness of towed meters (JOSEPH, 1955; DERA, 1963), which allow data to be taken while the ship is under way.

ATTENUANCE OF SEA WATER

Attenuance of pure water

A basic effect is due to the water itself. Progress in the investigation of this factor has been relatively slow, since the measurements — in common with scattering measurements — are handicapped by the manifest difficulty of preparing pure water.

JAMES and BIRGE (1938) have given a survey of research in this field. In spite of recurring instrumental defects, the results of these

TABLE XI

OBSERVED TRANSMITTANCE AND ATTENUATION COEFFICIENT, AND THEORETICAL SCATTERING COEFFICIENT FOR PURE WATER

Wavelength (nm)	Transmittance (%/m)	Attenuation coefficient (m^{-1})	Scattering coefficient (m^{-1})
	CLARKE and JAMES (1939)		LE GRAND (1939)
375	95.6	$45 \cdot 10^{-3}$	$6.64 \cdot 10^{-3}$
400	95.8	$43 \cdot 10^{-3}$	$5.03 \cdot 10^{-3}$
425	96.8	$33 \cdot 10^{-3}$	$3.89 \cdot 10^{-3}$
450	98.1	$19 \cdot 10^{-3}$	$3.05 \cdot 10^{-3}$
475	98.2	$18 \cdot 10^{-3}$	$2.43 \cdot 10^{-3}$
500	96.5	$36 \cdot 10^{-3}$	$1.97 \cdot 10^{-3}$
525	96.0	$41 \cdot 10^{-3}$	$1.60 \cdot 10^{-3}$
550	93.3	$69 \cdot 10^{-3}$	$1.33 \cdot 10^{-3}$
575	91.3	$91 \cdot 10^{-3}$	$1.11 \cdot 10^{-3}$
600	83.3	$186 \cdot 10^{-3}$	$0.93 \cdot 10^{-3}$
625	79.6	$228 \cdot 10^{-3}$	$0.78 \cdot 10^{-3}$
650	75.0	$288 \cdot 10^{-3}$	$0.67 \cdot 10^{-3}$
675	69.3	$367 \cdot 10^{-3}$	$0.58 \cdot 10^{-3}$
700	60.7	$500 \cdot 10^{-3}$	$0.49 \cdot 10^{-3}$
725	29	$1,240 \cdot 10^{-3}$	$0.43 \cdot 10^{-3}$
750	9	$2,400 \cdot 10^{-3}$	$0.38 \cdot 10^{-3}$
775	9	$2,400 \cdot 10^{-3}$	$0.33 \cdot 10^{-3}$
800	18	$2,050 \cdot 10^{-3}$	$0.29 \cdot 10^{-3}$

observations give evidence of the principal mechanism of attenuation. The blue is most penetrant whereas the red is strongly attenuated; there is a salient fall in transmittance from 560 to 600 nm.

It is generally thought that CLARKE and JAMES (1939) have been relatively successful in preparing pure water and that their values of attenuance for the visible region are representative (Table XI). A comparison between attenuance and scatterance (from Table I) indicates that the attenuance is primarily an absorption effect. It is important to note that water absorbs selectively, acting essentially as a monochromator of blue light. Only one absorption maximum, at 750–760 nm, occurs in the visible region; other absorption bands representing higher harmonics of the fundamental vibration frequency of the water molecule are generally weak. J. E. Tyler (personal communication, 1966) has detected a weak band around 520 nm.

In the infra-red range scattering can be disregarded compared to absorption, and the determination of attenuance reduced to an absorption measurement. In the distant infra-red difficulties arise in defining precisely the thin layers of water required for the absorption measurements. The infra-red attenuance is represented in Fig.17 by observations of the absorption coefficient in the region 0.7–2.5 μ published by CURCIO and PETTY (1951). The general increase of absorptance towards longer wavelengths is associated with the

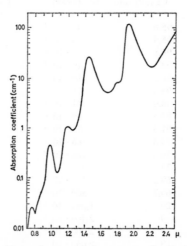

Fig.17. Absorption curve of pure water for the infrared.

occurrence of several absorption bands due to fundamental vibrational states of the water molecule or to combinations of these.

The determination of ultra-violet attenuance encounters difficulties and necessitates great precautions on account of the strong scattering and absorption arising even from traces of contaminations. The coefficients for the interval 220–400 nm obtained by LENOBLE and SAINT-GUILLY (1955) do not agree well with the values in Table XI, but are definitely greater. The significant results that arise from their study are the high transparency in the distant ultra-violet, which is consistent with radiance and irradiance measurements, and the absence of any absorption bands.

Little evidence is as yet forthcoming about the influence of temperature on the attenuation of radiant energy by pure water, at least for temperatures occurring in the sea. According to COLLINS (1925), there are no clear indications that the absorptance in the region 700—820 nm changes when the temperature is raised from 0.5° to 26° C. Increasing the temperature to 95° C brings out a clear temperature dependence in the infra-red inasmuch as the intensities of the absorption bands are enhanced and the positions of their maxima are slightly shifted toward shorter wavelengths. New and more complete studies on light attenuation by pure water are needed to ascertain the magnitude of the effect of sea water temperatures.

Attenuance of pure sea water

The question arises whether addition of sea salts to pure water causes a change in attenuance. After Berkefeld-filtering of clear ocean water, CLARKE and JAMES (1939) found no palpable differences between the attenuance of distilled water and that of the ocean water. Corroboratory results are presented by SULLIVAN (1963), who compared the absorption of distilled water with that of artificial sea water in the interval 580—790 nm. The substantive conclusion is that sea salts exert little influence on light attenuation. Nor do they act as absorbing media in the infra-red, as is shown by the careful investigation of VISSER (1967). The role of the salts in the ultra-violet has been studied by LENOBLE (1956a). They seem to cause a weak absorption which slowly increases toward shorter wavelengths without revealing the presence of absorption bands. These findings are supported by the observations of ARMSTRONG and BOALCH (1961).

Attenuance of particles

While pure sea water of given temperature displays an invariant light attenuation, other optically active components contribute a variable part to the attenuation of ordinary sea water. Attention is first drawn to the particulate matter which is found in highly variable concentration in the sea.

There is reason to believe that the attenuance caused by a mixture of particles of different composition would increase toward shorter wavelengths. Experimental evidence is furnished in particular by BURT (1958), who made measurements at thirteen wavelengths on samples drawn from the surface down to 1,170 m in the eastern tropical part of the Pacific Ocean. He was also successful in securing uncontaminated filtered samples of ocean water, for which the absorption coefficient due to dissolved substances was determined. By deducting this coefficient from the total attenuation coefficient we arrive at values of the attenuation coefficient due to scattering and absorption of particulate matter. The essential feature in the wavelength selective attenuation by particles is brought out by the curve in Fig.18 which is derived from Burt's observations in fairly turbid water. Assuming that scattering is virtually independent of wavelength (p.40), the major part of the selective effect is due to absorption.

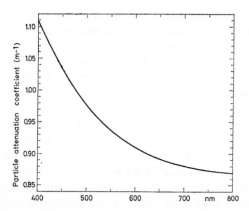

Fig.18. Light attenuance caused by particulate matter. (After BURT, 1958.)

Absorptance of dissolved organic substances

The optical action of the numerous organic substances dissolved in sea water is gradually becoming known. In a classical investigation, KALLE (1938) proved the significant role of soluble humus-like products which are yellow and some of which fluoresce in the blue when excited by ultra-violet radiation. The present state of research on this complex mixture of compounds, known under the collective name of "yellow substance", is summarized by KALLE (1962, 1966). Yellow substance is formed from carbohydrates by a "Maillard" reaction. The formation is favoured by heat, alcalic reaction and the presence of amino-acids, and leads to end products of yellow or brown melanoidines. Kalle concludes that in the sea, where carbohydrates and amino-acids are present, chiefly melanoidines with fluorescent matter as a by-product are likely to be formed, whereas non-fluorescent pheno-humic acid products of a browner colour seem to be mostly of continental origin (cf. SHAPIRO, 1957).

Large quantities of humus compounds are brought to the sea by rivers, especially in northern areas. This abundance is reduced in some degree through coagulation and precipitation mainly of the fine particulate or colloidal portion (LÜNEBURG, 1953; JERLOV, 1953b; Fig.74). JERLOV (1955a) has estimated that yellow substance, probably even in soluble form, during its passage and storing in the central Baltic loses about 10—15 % of its total concentration; the bulk of it is stable in the marine environment.

The production of yellow substance in the sea is a fact well supported by experiments. The established presence of yellow substance in the upwelling region west of South America proves its immediate marine origin, as this area is practically devoid of fresh-water supply from drainage and precipitation.

An absorption curve for a high concentration of yellow substance is adduced as a typical example of its wavelength selective effect (Fig.19). It follows that yellow substance should preferably be studied in the ultra-violet.

The extension of experiments to the far ultra-violet has proved fruitful, leading to important conclusions. FOGG and BOALCH (1958) have shown that ultra-violet absorbent substances are produced in filtrates of mass cultures of marine algae. The occurrence of a formative process is further supported by the finding of YENTSCH and REICHERT

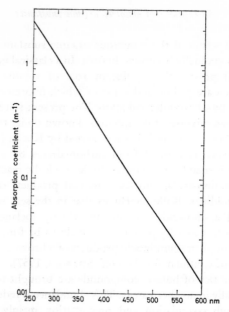

Fig.19. Absorption curve for yellow substance.

(1962) that the production of yellow substance is inversely proportional to the decomposition of the chloroplastic pigments. Certain components in the yellow substance display a distinct absorption peak at 250—265 nm (CHANU, 1959; YENTSCH and REICHERT, 1962). But the absorption curve in the range 220—400 nm for filtered Atlantic water shows a trend of steady increase towards shorter wavelengths as is evidenced by ARMSTRONG and BOALCH (1961). These workers have also drawn attention to the ultra-violet absorption due to volatile organic matter, probably of algal origin and to some degree due to nitrate, at least in deep water.

In situ determination of yellow substance

The in situ meter provided with colour filters enables us to arrive at values of the total selective absorption due to water, particles and yellow substance. JOSEPH (1949a) has pointed out that sufficient means to study the selective absorption are provided by recording in two spectral ranges in the red and in the ultra-violet. An abbreviated procedure makes a separation possible of the selective effect caused by particles and yellow substance respectively (JERLOV, 1955a). The method implies that the absorption coefficient of yellow substance at 380 nm, a_y, is expressed by the linear relation:

$$(c-c_w)_{380\text{nm}} - K(c-c_w)_{655\text{nm}} = a_y$$

where c_w pertains to attenuance by the water itself.

This approach assumes that the selective absorptance by particles is proportional to the particle attenuance in the red; it is taken for granted that the absorption of yellow substance vanishes in the red. The factor K is dependent on the average particle characteristics and is found to be constant for a given water mass. The usefulness of the method for the study of Bermuda waters has been demonstrated by IVANOFF et al. (1961).

Synopsis of attenuance components

Table XII has been prepared to show the factors which play a part in the attenuation by sea water and their dependence on the wave-

TABLE XII

SUMMARY OF ABSORPTION AND SCATTERING CHARACTERISTICS (WAVELENGTH $= \lambda$)

	Absorption		Scattering	
	character	λ-dependence	character	λ-dependence
Water	invariant at constant temp. and pressure	strong	invariant, small compared to absorption	λ^{-4}
Sea salts (inorganic)	negligible in the visible, weak in the ultraviolet	some increase towards short λ	–	
Yellow substance	variable	increase towards short λ	–	
Particulate matter	variable	increase towards short λ	variable	usually independent of λ

TABLE XIII

COMPARISON OF INHERENT PROPERTIES (m^{-1}) [1]

Region	Wave-length (nm)	$c - c_w$ observed	b_p observed	$a_p + b_p$	a_p	Δa_p	$a_p + a_y$	$\Delta(a_p + a_y)$	a_y observed	Δa_y	Reference
Sargasso Sea	440	0.05	0.04				0.01				
Caribbean Sea	655	0.06	0.06	0.06	0		0.00				
	440	0.09	0.06				0.03	0.03			JERLOV (1951)
Equator Central Pacific	440	0.09	0.05				0.04				
Romanche Deep	440	0.12	0.07				0.05				
Galapagos	655	0.11	0.07	0.11	0.04		0.04				
	440	0.24	0.08				0.16	0.12			
Off California	522	0.08	0.01				0.07				TYLER (1961a)
Off Peru (64 miles)	700	0.39		0.39					0		
	400	0.73		0.64		(0.25) *			0.09	0.09	
Galapagos	700	0.16		0.16					0		BURT (1958)
	400	0.25		0.21		(0.05 *			0.04	0.04	
Northwestern Galapagos	700	0.07		0.07					0		
	400	0.11		0.08		(0.04) *					

Location	λ (nm)	c	c_w	c_p	b_p	a_p	a_w	a	a_y	Δ	Reference
Continental slope	365	0.10			0.08				0.02	0.02	(1939)
Bermuda	655	0.10	0.10			(0.03)*		0.30	0	0.02	IVANOFF et al. (1961)
	380	0.20	0.17			(0.07)*			0.03	0.03	
Kattegat	655	0.23	0.15	0.23	0.08	0.19	0.08		0	0.11	JERLOV (1955a)
	380	0.54	0.16	0.44	0.27		0.38		0.11		
South Baltic Sea	655	0.27	0.20	0.27	0.07	0.21	0.07	0.89	0	0.68	
	380	1.15	0.21	0.49	0.28		0.96		0.68		
Bothnian Gulf	655	0.38	0.28	0.38	0.10	0.23	0.10	1.31	0	1.08	
	380	1.72	0.31	0.64	0.33		1.41		1.08		
Skagerrak	655					0.3		0.4		0.1	MALMBERG (1964)
	380										
North Atlantic	665								0	0.03	KALLE (1961)
	420								0.03	0.03	
North Sea	665								0.01	0.09	
	420								0.10		
Baltic Sea	665								0.02	0.31	
	420								0.33		

[1] c = total attenuation coefficient; c_w = attenuation coefficient for water; c_p = attenuation coefficient for particles; a_p = absorption coefficient for particles; b_p = scattering coefficient for particles; a_w = absorption coefficient for water; a_y = absorption coefficient for yellow substance; Δ = wavelength selectivity; $c = c_w + b_p + a_p + a_y$.

* If $\Delta b = 0$.

length. It claims only to give general, qualitative information about the parameters involved.

Regional comparison of inherent properties

Table XIII summarizes data which may serve to illustrate the web of relationships between the coefficients of inherent properties. These values derive from measurements of total attenuance in conjunction with determinations of the absorption coefficient for yellow substance, a_y, or the scattering coefficient for particles, b_p, or of both factors. Since coefficients for the different components are additive, other parameters tabulated are obtained from the relation:

$$c = c_w + b_p + a_p + a_y$$

using the notations of Table XIII. It is again assumed that the wavelength selectivity of particle scattering is $\Delta b = 0$, and therefore that:

$$\Delta(a_p + b_p) = \Delta a_p$$

In regard to the uncertainty in the absolute values of the coefficients, especially in b_p, the data obtained by different workers may be deemed reasonably consistent. Careful comparison is somewhat hampered by the fact that the selectivity is assigned to different wavelength intervals.

Some interest is focused on the close connection between $(c-c_w)_{red}$ and b_p, or ultimately between a_p and b_p. Understandably, these two parameters must be intimately related for given particle characteristics, as is also evidenced by measurements of IVANOFF et al. (1961) in Bermuda waters. The low value of a_p encountered in clear ocean water is in accordance with the theoretical findings that small and relatively transparent particles produce much more scattering than absorption (see MIDDLETON, 1952, p.36).

FLUORESCENCE

The initial research in the field of natural fluorescence of the sea was made by KALLE (1949). For a given water mass, he found a close relationship between fluorescence of filtered water samples and amount of yellow substance in accordance with the nature of fluorescent matter as a byproduct of the formation of yellow substance. In mainland water there is typically a higher proportion of yellow substance compared with fluorescent substance, and therefore the ratio of these two substances is a function of salinity (Chapter 14, p.166). The investigations by DUURSMA (1960) further indicate that the relatively low quantities of fluorescent matter in offshore waters are not of continental origin but originate from the breakdown of organic material. The mathematical side of the fluorescence problem has also been treated by DUURSMA and ROMMETS (1961).

Fluorescence can be determined in the laboratory with satisfactory accuracy. When excited by ultra-violet radiation, the water samples fluoresce in the blue at about 490 nm (KALLE, 1939b). Some information about the regional distribution of fluorescent substance is given in Table XIV. Ivanoff's data from the Tyrrhenian Sea can be re-

TABLE XIV

FLUORESCENSE (RELATIVE UNITS)

Region	Depth (m)	Fluorescense	Reference
Central Baltic Sea	0	1.5—1.8	
North Sea	0	0.5—1.0	
Red Sea	0	0.4	
Atlantic Ocean			
The Channel–New York	0	0.2—1.4	KALLE (1949)
Norwegian Sea			
Iceland—Jan Mayen	0	0.2	
	150	0.1	
	1,000	0.1	
Sargasso Sea	0	0.1	
Tyrrhenian Sea	0	0.12	
	50	0.14	IVANOFF (1964)
	75	0.19	
	100—3,000	0.20—0.22	
The Channel	0	1—2.5	
North Sea	0	3	KULLENBERG (1967b)
Skagerrak	0	6.5	
The Sound	0	14	

presented as depth profiles; these profiles exhibit an increase of fluorescence with depth down to 100 or 200 m and then become nearly constant.

PART II

Underwater Radiant Energy

CHAPTER 4

GLOBAL RADIATION INCIDENT ON THE SEA SURFACE

SPECTRAL DISTRIBUTIONS

Before entering into a detailed study of the main theme of under-water energy, proper consideration should be given to the primary energy source, i.e., the global radiation (from sun and sky) incident on the surface of the sea. The alteration of the sun's radiation in the atmosphere is due chiefly to scattering, which removes an appreciable part of the shortwave component of sunlight. Thus two components of a different nature are formed; the sun's radiation is directed and covers a large spectral range from 290 to 3,000 nm, whereas the sky-light is more diffuse and is dominant in the shortwave part of the spectrum. With a clear sky the spectral distribution of the global radiation at the sea surface is essentially a function of the air mass, i.e., of the solar elevation. To a minor degree, it is also dependent on the air turbidity. Clouds change the radiation in spectral distribution, especially in the infra-red.

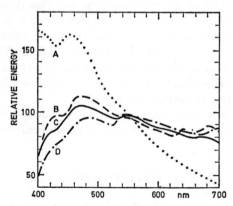

Fig.20. Average spectral distribution for (A) zenith sky, (B) sun+sky (horizontal plane), (C) overcast sky, (D) direct sunlight. (After TAYLOR and KERR, 1941.)

TABLE XV

SPECTRAL DISTRIBUTION OF IRRADIANCE FROM SUN AND SKY[1]

Wavelength	Solar altitude		
(nm)	15°	35°	65°
350	6	20	190
375	11	75	235
400	19	125	307
425	32	148	362
450	45	165	400
475	65	171	417
500	82	170	413
525	92	168	393
550	98	165	377
575	103	160	371
600	105	155	368
625	103	145	354
650	99	135	344
675	100	129	336
700	103	125	318
725	100	123	298
750	100	120	277

[1] Values for 15° and 35° according to ALBRECHT (1936); values for 65° according to KIMBALL (1924).

Our interest is focused chiefly on the visible light — in general called daylight — which penetrates into the sea. Fine details in the spectral distribution serve no purpose in this connection. Some basic data on the irradiance in the range 350–750 nm for different solar elevations are presented in Table XV. TAYLOR and KERR (1941) have given average spectral distributions for some phases of daylight representing direct sunlight, sunlight plus skylight on a horizontal plane, overcast sky, and zenith sky (Fig.20).

Information about the whole spectrum is presented in Fig.51, which exhibits the numerous absorption bands occurring in the distribution.

ANGULAR DISTRIBUTIONS

The radiance distribution of a clear sky shows a marked maximum near the sun, as is illustrated in Fig.21. The presence of clouds is apt

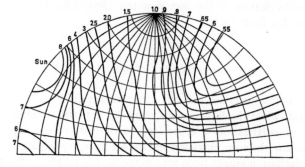

Fig.21. Radiance distribution for a clear sky.

to change the distribution of skylight drastically. The radiance from most overcast skies can be represented by a cardioidal distribution according to the empirical formula of MOON and SPENCER (1942):

$$L(i) = L(\tfrac{1}{2}\pi)(1+2 \cos i) \qquad (24)$$

In the treatment of problems of reflection, refraction and penetration of radiant energy, it is good methodology to distinguish sunlight and skylight. In consequence, the ratio of sky radiation to the global radiation becomes a significant factor. The major features in the trend of this ratio as a function of wavelength and solar elevation are clearly brought out in Fig.22, which was derived by SAUBERER and RUTTNER (1941) on the basis of KIMBALL's (1924) data. A

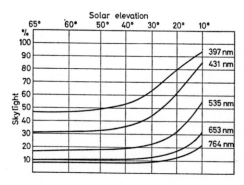

Fig. 22. Percentage of skylight in the global radiation as a function of solar elevation. (After SAUBERER and RUTTNER, 1941.)

noteworthy feature is the fact that the ultra-violet from the sky matches that from the sun at low elevations.

POLARIZATION

The familiar facts are that the direct energy from the sun is unpolarized, while the light from a clear sky is partly polarized. The degree of polarization is dependent on the part of the sky under observation, the solar elevation and the air turbidity (SEKERA, 1957). The polarization ranges from zero in the neutral points to maximum values of over 90 % at about 90° from the sun in the vertical plane through the observation point and the sun. The position of the Arago neutral point is in the sun vertical on the antisolar side; the Babinet point and the Brewster point are found above and below the sun. It may be added that clouds have a strong depolarizing effect.

CHAPTER 5

REFLECTION AT THE SEA SURFACE

THEORY

Reflectance for direct radiation

The reflectance for the electric vector of the radiation resolved into components parallel and perpendicular to the plane of incidence, is given by Fresnel's equations:

$$\rho_{\parallel} = \frac{tg^2(i-j)}{tg^2(i+j)} \qquad (25)$$

$$\rho_{\perp} = \frac{\sin^2(i-j)}{\sin^2(i+j)} \qquad (26)$$

where i is the angle of incidence and j is the angle of refraction. The reflected ray is in the plane of incidence and the angle of reflection is equal to i.

Since the solar radiation is unpolarized, its reflectance may be taken as a mean value of the above quantities:

$$\rho_s = \frac{1}{2} \left| \frac{\sin^2(i-j)}{\sin^2(i+j)} + \frac{tg^2(i-j)}{tg^2(i+j)} \right| \qquad (27)$$

For normal incidence the distinction between parallel and perpendicular components disappears, and the equation reduces to:

$$\rho_{\parallel} = \rho_{\perp} = \rho_s = \frac{(n-1)^2}{(n+1)^2}$$

If $i+j = 90°$ we have from eq.33:

$$tg\, i = n \qquad \text{(Brewster's law)} \qquad (28)$$

and only light oscillating perpendicular to the plane of incidence is reflected. This occurs at a water surface ($n = \frac{4}{3}$) for $i = 53°.1$, and in this case:

$$\rho_s = \frac{1}{2} \left(\frac{n^2-1}{n^2+1} \right)^2$$

Values of the Fresnel reflectance according to the above equations are tabulated as functions of the solar elevation (Table XVI).

Linearly polarized light which is completely internally reflected suffers a phase change between the parallel and perpendicular components giving rise to elliptically polarized light. WATERMAN (1954) and IVANOFF and WATERMAN (1958a) have proved that elliptically polarized light occurs just below the water surface in lines of sight differing from the vertical by less than the critical angle (see Chapter 6).

TABLE XVI

REFLECTANCE OF RADIATION AGAINST A CALM SURFACE

Angle of incidence ($i°$)	Reflectance (%)		
	$\rho_{\parallel}$	$\rho_{\perp}$	ρ_s
0	2.0	2.0	2.0
5	2.0	2.1	2.0
10	1.9	2.1	2.0
15	1.8	2.3	2.0
20	1.7	2.5	2.1
25	1.4	2.7	2.1
30	1.2	3.1	2.1
35	0.9	3.6	2.3
40	0.6	4.3	2.4
45	0.3	5.3	2.8
50	0.1	6.7	3.4
55	0.2	8.6	4.4
60	0.4	11.5	5.9
65	1.7	15.8	8.7
70	4.7	21.9	13.3
75	11.0	31.3	21.2
80	24.0	45.9	34.9
85	49.3	67.4	58.3
90	100	100	100

Reflectance for diffuse radiation

The reflection of the diffuse component is more difficult to express quantitatively. A first approximation considers diffuse light of equal radiance from all directions L of the sky. The reflectance $\rho(i)$ for the angle of incidence i is taken from the Fresnel equations. It follows from the definition of reflectance and from eq.5 that:

$$\rho_d = \frac{2\pi \int_0^{\frac{1}{2}\pi} \rho(i)L \sin i \cos i \, di}{2\pi \int_0^{\frac{1}{2}\pi} L \sin i \cos i \, di} = \int_0^{\frac{1}{2}\pi} \rho(i) \sin 2i \, di \qquad (29)$$

Several workers have evaluated this integral for a smooth water surface using Fresnel's reflectance. The consistent value is found to be 6.6 % (see BURT, 1954a).

For the reflectance in the case of a cardinal distribution of sky radiation (eq.24), PREISENDORFER (1957) has given an exact solution which yields 5.2 %.

Reflectance for global radiation

When dealing with the reflectance of global radiation we have to treat separately the reflectance of direct energy or solar radiation, ρ_s, and that of sky radiation, ρ_d.

The total reflectance is expressed as the sum:

$$\rho = \frac{E_r}{E} = \rho_s(1-n) + \rho_d n \qquad (30)$$

where E and E_r are the incident and reflected irradiance respectively, and n is the significant ratio of sky radiation to global radiation.

The result of computations of the reflected energy from eq.30 using ρ_s-values from eq.27 and $\rho_d = 0.066$ and assuming the incoming radiation to be a given function of the solar elevation, is illustrated, for example, by the set of curves for several n-values in Fig.23 (NEUMANN and HOLLMAN, 1961). The curve for solar radiation only ($n = 0$) develops a prominent maximum at 20° as well as a slight minimum at 50°. The intersection point of the curves at 29° represents the case of $\rho_s = \rho_d = 0.066$.

The assumption of uniform sky radiation is inadequate, and more realistic approaches have been made. COX and MUNK (1956) have

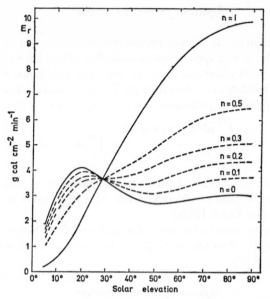

Fig.23. Amount of reflected energy for different portions *n* of diffuse radiation in the global radiation. (After NEUMANN and HOLLMAN, 1961.)

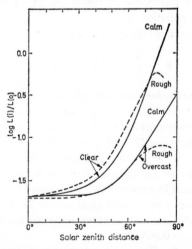

Fig.24. Reflected radiance *L(i)* divided by the sky radiance at zenith for calm weather and for a Beaufort 4 wind. (After COX and MUNK, 1956.)

also employed a semi-empirical model and considered a clear tropical sky on the basis of observations at Bocaiuva, Brazil, for the sun at a zenith angle of 60°. They made the simple assumption that the reflectance is a function of the zenith angle only, ignoring the increased radiance near the sun (Fig.21). Their results for clear and overcast sky conditions are presented in Fig.24.

Effect of waves

The complete investigation of the interaction of light with the sea surface confronts us with the additional problem of reflection from a wind-roughened surface. The following changes in reflection are immediately realized. With high solar elevations the angle of incidence will be increased on an average, whereas it will be decreased for low elevations. The former effect is not important, as the reflectance does not vary much with the solar elevation if this is high. In contrast, the reflectance for a low sun is drastically reduced by wave action. This principal feature was first formulated and investigated by LE GRAND (1939). It appears that the reflectance is independent of the presence of waves in some intermediate elevation interval. BURT (1954a), employing a semi-theoretical model, actually found that such independence occurs somewhere between solar elevations of 10° and 30°.

The thorough interpretation of the wind effect given by COX and MUNK (1956) also takes into account shadowing and multiple reflections for a low sun. Their radiance curves in Fig.25 demonstrate in essence that the wave action becomes a factor for solar elevations

TABLE XVII

REFLECTANCE (%) OF THE SEA FOR SKYLIGHT

Sky	Sea		
	Smooth	Rough	
		BURT (1954a)	COX and MUNK (1956)
Uniform	6.6	5.7	5.0−5.5
Overcast	5.2	4.8	4.3−4.7

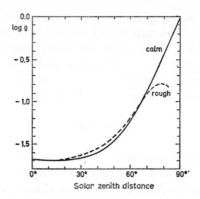

Fig.25. Reflectance of solar radiation from a flat surface and from a surface roughened by a Beaufort 4 wind. (After Cox and MUNK, 1956.)

below 20°. GRIŠČENKO (1959) and HISHIDA and KISHINO (1965) have demonstrated similar wave effects at low angles. As expected, the reflection of sky light is less affected by rough sea (Table XVII). Cox and Munk point out that with an absolutely flat sea the horizon would not be visible. Actually the sea always contrasts with the sky and becomes darker when the wind increases. The shadowing is also examined by LAUSCHER (1955), who computed data which amply illustrate the irregular reflection pattern from a wave of maximal steepness (Michell wave).

Glitter of the sea

Glitter is a phenomenon bearing upon reflection of solar radiation. This special aspect of reflection has given rise to much speculation. The glitter pattern being open to everyone's observation, it has in popular speech been given poetic names such as "the road to happiness" (SHOULEIKIN, 1941) or "the golden bridge" (STELENAU, 1961). The glitter arises when a flat surface is roughened by wind and the image of the sun formed by specular reflection explodes into glittering points. This is because water facets occur with an orientation so as to reflect sunlight to the observer. Increasing roughness will enlarge the width of the glittering band. The phenomenon is most spectacular at solar elevations of 30—35° (cf. Fig.23). The pattern becomes narrower when the sun sets.

The distribution of radiance of glitter has been the subject of theoretical treatment with a view to estimating the slopes of the sea surface. The interested reader may consult the original papers by HULBURT (1934), DUNTLEY (1952), COX and MUNK (1956), SCHOOLEY (1961), and MULLAMAA (1964b).

The latter has also considered the polarization of the reflected glitter, which is shown to be dependent both on solar elevation and on the direction of reflection. The polarization at the maximum radiance is near zero at $i = 0°$ and increases with zenith distance to 100 % at $i = 35—45°$, subsequently decreasing to 20 % at $i = 90°$.

CONCEPT OF ALBEDO

In order to scrutinize reflection events and secure adequate definitions, the following symbols are pertinent:

E_{ad} = downward irradiance in air.
E_{au} = upward irradiance in air.
E_{wd} = downward irradiance in water.
E_{wu} = upward irradiance in water.

Since reflection against the sea surface takes place from above as well as from below, two kinds of reflectance are distinguished: (1) ρ_a = reflectance in air; and (2) ρ_w = reflectance in water.

The albedo A of the sea is defined as the ratio of the energy leaving the sea to that falling on it:

$$A = \frac{E_{au}}{E_{ad}} \tag{31}$$

The above definitions yield the following identities:

$$E_{ad}-E_{au} = E_{wd}-E_{wu}$$
$$E_{au} = \rho_a E_{ad}+E_{wu}-\rho_w E_{wu}$$

From eq.31 the albedo may therefore be written:

$$A = \rho_a+(1-\rho_w)\frac{E_{wu}}{E_{ad}} \tag{32}$$

Some confusion in reflection studies has resulted from failure to distinguish the reflection (at a surface) in a strict sense, namely ρ_a, and the albedo which is the sum of ρ_a and the percentage of light back-scattered from the sea. Furthermore, the factor ρ_w must be accounted for. Because of the relatively small variation of the scattering function in the back-scatter field, we can assume in a first approximation that the upwelling light is completely diffuse and unpolarized. Because Fresnel reflection beneath the surface involves total reflection in the angle interval 48.6—90°, integration of eq.29 yields $\rho_w = 48\%$. Hence it is not permissible to neglect this factor as most workers have done.

EXPERIMENTAL VALUES OF REFLECTANCE

A selection among the multitude of reflection observations is called for. The systematic studies of albedo as a function of various parameters made by ANDERSON (1954) and FORŠ (1954) will be our primary references. The Lake Hefner results suggest that the albedo under clear skies is only weakly dependent on wind speed and air mass turbidity, including the effects of clouds. We may infer that the albedo is primarily a function of solar altitude. Even with a low stratus cloud cover, the dependence on the position of the sun persists. This is consistent with the findings of NEIBURGER (1948), but conflicts with earlier statements (Chapter 4).

Table XVIII shows the true reflectance for a flat level surface and clear sky. These values have been drawn chiefly from Anderson's results with due correction for the existing low shortwave back-scattering from the water of Lake Hefner.

In rough weather it is difficult to distinguish between the true reflectance and the shortwave light back-scattered from the sea. White caps and air bubbles in the surface layer contribute greatly to the albedo. Experiments have verified the reduction of reflectance at low solar elevations owing to wave action. The present author found

TABLE XVIII

REFLECTANCE OF UNPOLARIZED RADIANT ENERGY (SUN+SKY) FROM A HORIZONTAL WATER SURFACE

Solar altitude (°)	90	60	50	40	30	20	10	5
Reflectance (%)	3	3	3	4	6	12	27	42

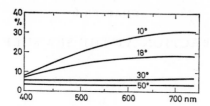

Fig.26. Reflectance (%) of global radiation for different solar elevations as a function of wavelength. Corrected for cosine error of the collector.
(After SAUBERER and RUTTNER, 1941.)

that a flat sea surface is a barrier to the light from a distant lighthouse tower, whereas the reflection of this light from a rough surface is remarkably low.

DISPERSION OF REFLECTION

It is established by observations that for solar elevation below 30° a dependence of reflection of irradiance on wavelength is developed (Fig.26). SAUBERER and RUTTNER (1941) have given the right explanation of this effect which — since the dispersion of light reflection is only 6% — must be associated with the amount of diffuse light in the global light. This is 90% in the violet and 22% in the red for a solar elevation of 10° (Fig.22). The average angle of incidence is thus much less for the violet than for the red, which accounts for the stated difference in reflection.

CHAPTER 6

REFRACTION AT THE SEA SURFACE

REFRACTION LAW

The interface between air and sea is a boundary between two media of different optical density. An electromagnetic wave falling on the surface decomposes into two waves; one is refracted and proceeds into the sea, the other is reflected and propagates back into the air (Fig.27).

The law of refraction is:

$$\frac{\sin i}{\sin j} = n \tag{33}$$

a relation known as Snell's law. The angles i and j are defined so as to describe a refracted wave as being in the same plane as the incident wave. For definiteness we may take the refractive index n of sea water relative to air to be $\frac{4}{3}$. From a geophysical point of view there is no need to account for the variation of the index with temperature, salinity and wavelength (Chapter 2, p.25).

For the case of grazing incidence ($i = 90°$) a limiting angle of refraction $j = 48.5°$ is obtained. As seen from the sea, the sky dome is compressed into a cone of half-angle 48.5°. If they form an angle of more than 48.5° with the vertical, upward travelling rays are totally reflected at the surface (Fig.27).

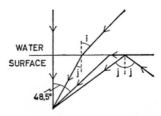

Fig.27. Refraction and total internal reflection at the sea surface.

Refraction is associated with polarization according to Fresnel's formulae. Direct sunlight penetrating into the water becomes partly polarized. Calculations by MULLAMAA (1964a) testify that the degree of polarization increases with the sun's zenith distance and reaches magnitudes as great as 27 % during sunset.

The linearity of skylight polarization remains unchanged by refraction though there is a rotation of the plane of oscillation.

CHANGE OF RADIANCE AND IRRADIANCE AT THE SURFACE

It follows from simple geometrical considerations that the radiance L_w below water of refractive index n is n^2 times the radiance L_a in air reduced by reflection losses at the surface (GERSHUN, 1939):

$$L_w = n^2(1-\rho)L_a \tag{34}$$

The downward irradiance in air and in water are respectively:

$$dE_a = L_a \cos i\,d\omega = L_a \cos i \sin i\,d\phi\,di$$
$$dE_w = L_w \cos j\,d\omega = L_w \cos j \sin j\,d\phi\,dj$$

From eq.33 and 34 it follows that:

$$dE_w = (1-\rho)dE_a \tag{35}$$

which verifies the obvious fact that the interface between air and water changes irradiance on a plane parallel to the interface by reflection only.

EFFECT OF WAVES ON REFRACTION

Refraction according to Fig.27 is described by Snell's law only in the ideal case of a flat surface. Waves cause fluctuations of the direction of refracted rays. Deviations of the direction of maximum radiance can amount to as much as ± 15 % according to theoretical deductions of MULLAMAA (1964a). Because of wave action, the image of the sun as seen from beneath the surface disintegrates into a glitter pattern with features different from those of the reflected glitter. The refracted glitter subtends a smaller angle and is of the order of 1,000 times more intense than the reflected glitter. Due to lens action of individual waves, the flashes can attain a level dangerously high for the upwardly directed human eye. According to Cox and MUNK (1956) the refracted glitter, in contrast to the reflected, expands and dims when the sun approaches the horizon.

CHAPTER 7

THEORY OF RADIATIVE TRANSFER IN THE SEA

The penetration and distribution of underwater radiant energy is determined by absorption and scattering processes the natures of which have been the subject of preceding chapters. From the change of the light field investigated by radiance measurements, complete information is derived about the inherent properties of the water. It should be pointed out, however, that we have so far dealt with relatively small transmittance distances and with small scattering volumes. When light propagates to great depths, selective absorption will have a tremendous effect and the scattering volumes will be so large that the full complexities of multiple scattering become important. Theoretical studies which take account only of primary scattering must be regarded only as a first approximation for turbid surface water. The various avenues of approach to the theoretical problems which have lead to our present comprehension of underwater radiative transfer are outlined below with a view to presenting also deductions made under simplifying assumptions. PREISENDORFER (1965) has recently published a mathematical treatise on all phases of the radiative transfer problem.

The theoretical study of radiative transfer in the sea was initiated by LE GRAND (1939). His approach to the irradiance problem considers isotropic scattering produced by sun rays only. The predicted irradiance as a function of depth brings out the essential feature that the monochromatic irradiance E is less attenuated in the upper layers than in deeper layers, so that the logarithmic curve, i.e., $ln\ E$ plotted against z, shows a curvature. Similar simple models employing Rayleigh scattering have been investigated in considerable detail (LAUSCHER, 1947; TAKENOUTI, 1949; MUKAI, 1959). However, in the light of facts proving the dominance of forward scattering, more realistic assumptions about the scattering function are required.

SIMPLE INTEGRATION OF SCATTERED LIGHT

As an introduction, we shall investigate the general simple model without making so far any assumptions about the scattering function. It is postulated that in the near-surface layer the sunlight is the only source of scattering, and that multiple scattering may be disregarded. The radiance due to scattered light may then be found by simple integration.

Let E be the irradiance just below the water surface (Fig.28). The small volume element dv at P is irradiated by:

$$E \sec j \, e^{-cx \sec j}$$

The volume element scatters intensity dI in the direction (θ, ϕ) which forms an angle α to the incident beam. If the azimuth is ϕ ($\phi = 0°$ for the plane of incidence), the angle α is obtained from the expression:

$$\cos \alpha = \cos j \cos \theta + \sin j \sin \theta \cos \phi$$

The scattered intensity is by definition:

$$dI = E \sec j \, e^{-cx \sec j} \, \beta(\alpha) dv$$

and the irradiance at Q on a plane normal to PQ is:

$$dE_{sc} = E \sec j \, e^{-cx \sec j} \, \beta(\alpha) dv \cdot \frac{1}{r^2} e^{-cr}$$

where:

$$dv = r^2 d\omega \, dr.$$

Considering that at Q the radiance $L_r = dE_{sc}/d\omega$ we obtain the

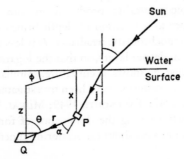

Fig. 28. Geometry for evaluating radiance of scattered light.

radiance $L(\theta)$ in the direction θ in the upper hemisphere ($\theta = 0$ to $\pi/2$) and in the vertical plane of the sun by integration with respect to r from 0 to $z \sec \theta$.

$$L(\theta) = E \sec j \frac{\beta(\theta - j)}{c} \frac{\sec \theta}{\sec \theta - \sec j} (e^{-cz \sec j} - e^{-cz \sec \theta}) \qquad (36)$$

The radiance is zero at the surface and is maximum at a depth z_m, independent of the scattering function. Maximization yields the value:

$$z_m = \frac{1}{c} \frac{ln \sec \theta - ln \sec j}{\sec \theta - \sec j} \qquad (37)$$

This formula was deduced by Lauscher who also points out that for $\theta = j$ it reduces to:

$$z_m = \frac{1}{c} \cos j$$

For the lower hemisphere, integration is performed in the vertical plane of the sun from the depth z to infinite depths. This yields:

$$L(\theta) = E \sec j \frac{\beta(\theta - j)}{c} \frac{\sec \theta}{\sec \theta - \sec j} e^{-cz \sec j} \qquad (38)$$

In this case the logarithmic curve is a straight line.

The downward irradiance of scattered light on a horizontal surface at Q is given by:

$$dE_{sc} = E \sec j\, e^{-cz \sec j}\, \beta(\alpha) \sin \theta \cos \theta\, e^{-cr}\, d\phi\, d\theta\, dr$$

and, after integration with respect to r from 0 to $z \sec \theta$, by:

$$E_{sc} = E \sec j\, e^{-cz \sec j} \frac{1}{c} \int_0^{2\pi} \int_0^{\frac{1}{2}\pi} \frac{\beta(\alpha) \sin \theta}{\sec \theta - \sec j}$$

$$(1 - e^{-cz(\sec \theta - \sec j)}) d\phi\, d\theta$$

If skylight is neglected, the total irradiance E_d is the sum of the scattered and the direct irradiances at the depth z, namely:

$$E_d = E\, e^{-cz \sec j} \left(1 + \frac{\sec j}{c} \int_0^{2\pi} \int_0^{\frac{1}{2}\pi} \frac{\beta(\alpha) \sin \theta}{\sec \theta - \sec j}\right.$$

$$\left. (1 - e^{-cz(\sec \theta - \sec j)}) d\phi\, d\theta \right) \qquad (39)$$

For a zenith sun ($j = 0$) and for small optical depths ($cz \to 0$) the equation takes the simple form:

$$E_d = E\,e^{-cz}\left(1 + 2\pi z \int_0^{\frac{1}{2}\pi} \beta(\theta)\,\sin\theta\,d\theta\right)$$

Because of the small percentage of back-scatter in the total function it is permissible to write:

$$E_d = E\,e^{-cz}(1 + bz) = E\,e^{-cz + bz} = E\,e^{-az} \tag{40}$$

which suggests that irradiance attenuation in the surface stratum is identified as absorption only.

A general expression for upward irradiance which is entirely scattered light is found by integrating to infinite depths:

$$E_u = E\,\sec j\,e^{-cz\,\sec j} \cdot \frac{1}{c} \int_0^{2\pi} \int_0^{\frac{1}{2}\pi} \frac{\beta(\alpha)\,\sin\theta}{\sec\theta + \sec j}\,d\phi\,d\theta \tag{41}$$

SEMI-EMPIRICAL MODEL

A substantial improvement of the radiance model's consistency with observations is gained by inserting measured values of the scattering function into the equations (JERLOV and FUKUDA, 1960). Crucial tests were made for turbid water having the inherent properties $c = 0.5$ and $b = 0.3$. The evaluated maximum radiance for downward scattered light is found at the greatest depth, 1.9 m, for $\theta = 0$ and at the surface for $\theta = 90$.

Upward-scattered light is distributed not only in the lower hemisphere but also in the upper, since it is reflected at the sea surface (Fig.29). Reflection takes place between $+90$ and $-90°$, and total reflection in the intervals $+48.6°$ to $+90°$ and $-48.6°$ to $-90°$ (horizontal surface). This leads to conspicuous peaks in the computed curves at $+90°$ and $-90°$, as was first recognized by TYLER (1958). A slight maximum at $-150°$ is ascribed to back-scattering through $180°$ from the sun's position ($+30°$).

The final step is to add underwater sunlight and skylight (Chapters 4 and 6) to the field of radiance created by scattering. The structure of the total light field thus built up exhibits, in spite of its complexity, a gratifying agreement with the experimental findings (Fig.39).

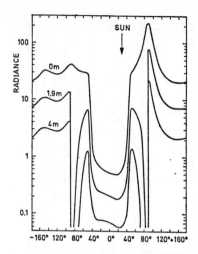

Fig.29. Radiance of upwardly scattered light. Reflection takes place between $+90°$ and $-90°$, and total reflection from $+48°.6°$ to $+90°$ and from $-48°.6°$ to $-90°$. (After Jerlov and Fukuda, 1960.)

RELATION BETWEEN DOWNWARD AND UPWARD IRRADIANCE

It follows from the law of conservation of energy that the divergence of the irradiance vector in an absorbing medium is related to the absorption coefficient in the following way (Gershun, 1936):

$$\operatorname{div} E = -aE_o \tag{42}$$

For the sea, where horizontal variations of irradiance are small, eq.42 takes the form:

$$\frac{\mathrm{d}(E_d - E_u)}{\mathrm{d}z} = -aE_o \tag{43}$$

This allows determination of the absorption coefficient from observed quantities, the scalar irradiance E_o being obtained from the measured spherical irradiance E_s according to previous definitions.

Considering that E_u is small compared with E_d, eq.43 reduces to eq.40 for zenith sun in the surface stratum.

A great deal of emphasis has been laid on adequate derivations of the irradiance ratio $R = E_u/E_d$ from the classical two-flow model

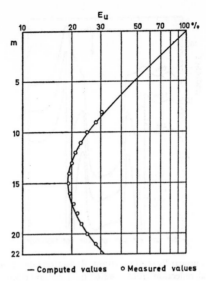

Fig.30. Minimum in the upward irradiance over a highly reflecting sand bottom in the Skagerrak. (After JOSEPH, 1950.)

(WHITNEY, 1938; POOLE, 1945; LENOBLE, 1956b; PELEVIN, 1966; KOZLYANINOV and PELEVIN, 1966). By assuming in first approximation that the backscattering function, β_b, is constant between 90° and 180° this model yields:

$$R = 2\pi(\beta_b/c)(1 - ln\ 2)e^{-bz} \simeq 1.2(\beta_b/c)e^{-bz} \tag{44}$$

for zenith sun in the surface layer. This states not only the obvious fact that the ratio is proportional to the back-scattering, but also that it is attenuated by the term e^{-bz} in the surface stratum. The model may be applied to advantage under conditions of high back-scattering by particles. JOSEPH (1950) has also shown that a simple two-flow system readily describes the change of upward irradiance with depth over a light-reflecting bottom in conformity to observations (Fig.30).

RADIATIVE TRANSFER EQUATION

A precise formulation of radiative transfer in an absorbing and scattering medium such as the sea is given by the classical equation:

$$\frac{\mathrm{d}L(z, \theta, \phi)}{\mathrm{d}r} = -cL(z, \theta, \phi) + L_*(z, \theta, \phi) \qquad (45)$$

The first term on the right represents loss by attenuation, the second gain by scattering. The latter quantity, called the path function, involves every volume element in the sea as a source of scattering and is generalized in the form:

$$L_*(z, \theta, \phi) = \int_{\phi'=0}^{2\pi} \int_{\theta'=0}^{\pi} \beta(\theta, \phi; \theta', \phi') L(z, \theta', \phi') \sin \theta' \, \mathrm{d}\theta' \, \mathrm{d}\phi' \qquad (46)$$

This integro-differential equation lends itself to diverse mathematical treatments. Its potentialities for describing the underwater light field has been explored at the Visibility Laboratory (San Diego) taking into account multiple scattering of limited order. DUNTLEY (1963) mentions that in this case the equation is solved in practice by iterative procedures on the largest electronic computers.

An investigation by PREISENDORFER (1961) suggests definitions which lead to a better understanding of the "inherent properties" involved in the transfer. Eq.45 may be written:

$$c = \frac{L_*}{L} - \frac{1}{L} \cdot \frac{\mathrm{d}L}{\mathrm{d}r}$$

It is possible by instrumental means to minimize L_* so that:

$$c = -\frac{1}{L} \cdot \frac{\mathrm{d}L}{\mathrm{d}r}$$

This applies to the beam transmittance meter in which radiance attenuance over a fixed distance is measured.

Another special case may be specified by noting that radiance along a horizontal path in the sea is generally constant. With $\mathrm{d}L/\mathrm{d}r = 0$, it is found that:

$$c = \frac{L_*}{L}$$

The experimental arrangement which satisfies this equation would be to take, in the same horizontal direction, records of the actual radiance L and of the radiance from a black target which yields L_*. This measuring principle was introduced by LE GRAND (1939) in his "l'écran noir".

The classical eq.45 can also be used to derive Gershun's eq.42. Considering that $z = -r \cos \theta$, i.e., that θ is the angle between zenith and the motion of the flux, integrating eq.45 over the sphere yields:

$$\frac{\mathrm{d}(E_d - E_u)}{\mathrm{d}z} = -cE_o + bE_o = -aE_o$$

where E_0 is the scalar irradiance.

RADIANCE MODEL OF THE VISIBILITY LABORATORY

In a series of papers, Preisendorfer has brought to completion the theoretical model of radiance distribution in the sea. His work, stimulated by DUNTLEY's (1948) original findings, is summarized in a comprehensive paper of PREISENDORFER (1964). The model considers a target point at depth z_t and at a distance r from the observation point at depth z. The path has the direction (θ, ϕ) where θ is the angle between the zenith and the motion of the flux. Hence we have $z_t - z = r \cos \theta$. The field radiance is measured by pointing a radiance meter at depth z in the direction $(\pi - \theta, \phi + \pi)$.

For an optically uniform medium an integration of eq.45 along the path (z_t, θ, ϕ, r) yields the following expression for the apparent radiance L_r of the target:

$$L_r(z, \theta, \phi) = L_0(z_t, \theta, \phi)e^{-cr} + \int_0^r L_*(z', \theta, \phi)e^{-c(r-r')} \, \mathrm{d}r' \qquad (47)$$

where L_o is the inherent radiance of the target and $z' = z_t - r' \cos \theta$. The apparent radiance L_r may thus be written as the sum of a transmitted inherent radiance and a path radiance which consists of flux scattered into the direction (θ, ϕ) at each point of the path (z_t, θ, ϕ, r) and then transmitted to the observation point.

Preisendorfer has shown that an approximate form for $L_*(z, \theta, \phi)$ can be obtained from the two-flow Schuster equations for irradiance:

$$L_*(z, \theta, \phi) = L_*(0, \theta, \phi)e^{-Kz} \qquad (48)$$

where K is independent of depth.

A combination of eq.47 and 48 results in the following relation:

$$L_r(z, \theta, \phi) = L_0(z_t, \theta, \phi)e^{-cr} + \frac{L_*(z, \theta, \phi)}{c + K \cos \theta}[1 - e^{-(c + K \cos \theta)r}] \qquad (49)$$

It is characteristic of this theory of radiative transfer that no mathematical expression for the scattering function is introduced or tested but that the whole path function is treated as a parameter with defined properties.

The validity of the formulas for the observed radiance distribution has been investigated by TYLER (1960a) on the basis of his complete set of accurate radiance data from Lake Pend Oreille. The key problem in such an application is to evaluate the path function L_*. Tyler starts from eq.49. For a path of sight directed at the zenith ($\theta = 180°$, $\phi = 0°$), this reduces to:

$$L(z) = L_o e^{-cz} + \frac{L_*(z)}{c-K}(1 - e^{-(c-K)z}) \tag{50}$$

where L_o denotes the radiance of the zenith sky just below the surface.

For the path of sight directed downward ($\theta = \phi = 0$, $L_o = 0$ for $r = \infty$), we have the corresponding relation:

$$L(z) = \frac{L_*(z)}{c+K} \tag{51}$$

The attenuation of the diffuse light $L_*(z)$ is described by eq.48:

$$L_*(z) = L_*(0)e^{-Kz}. \tag{52}$$

It follows that:

$$L(z) = L_o e^{-cz} + \frac{L_*(0)e^{-Kz}}{c-K}(1 - e^{-(c-K)z}) \tag{53}$$

The procedure involves determining $L_*(z)$ from experimental data from a single depth employing eq.50 and from $L_*(0)$ given by eq.51. This allows us to evaluate $L(z)$ for all depths by means of eq.53. The net result of the computations compares well with observations (Fig.40).

CHANDRASEKHAR'S METHOD

LENOBLE (1958a, 1961a, 1963) has adopted the method developed by CHANDRASEKHAR (1950). The equation of transfer is expressed in the form:

$$\cos\theta \frac{dL(z,\theta,\phi)}{dz} = cL(z,\theta,\phi) - \beta(\theta,\phi;\theta_o,\phi_o)E_i e^{cz\sec\theta_o}$$

$$-\int_{\theta'=0}^{\pi} \int_{\phi'=0}^{2\pi} \beta(\theta,\phi;\theta',\phi')L(z,\theta,\phi)\sin\theta'\,d\theta'\,d\phi' \quad (54)$$

where E_i is the irradiance produced by the sunlight on a plane perpendicular to its propagation in the water (θ_o,ϕ_o). Here the angle θ is measured from the zenith to the direction of measurement.

The equation describes a mixed light field composed of direct sunlight and diffuse light. By omitting the last term on the right-hand side one obtains a first approximation for primary scattering only which is identical to that obtained from the simple model discussed on p.82.

The theory presumes a known law of scattering. For a scattering medium of large particles, the scattering function can be developed into a series of Legendre polynomials of the form:

$$\frac{b}{4\pi}\sum_{n=0}^{N}\alpha_n P_n(\cos\theta)$$

The resulting N integro-differential equations are solved by the method of discrete ordinates. An alternative is to approximate the radiance by a development in a series of spherical harmonics.

In practice, Lenoble has truncated the above series, retaining only three terms ($N = 2$), and expressing the scattering function by:

$$\beta(\theta) = \frac{b}{4\pi}\left(1 + 1.73\,P_1(\cos\theta) + P_2(\cos\theta)\right) \quad (55)$$

This approach is of course much better adapted to the real shape of the function than are assumptions of isotropic and Rayleigh scattering. Confronted with experiments, it has proved fruitful and has allowed the derivation of inherent properties in the ultra-violet region (Table XIX). SCHELLENBERG (1963) has contributed a penetrating analysis of eq.54, and has also utilized an asymmetric β function of the form:

$$\beta(\theta) = \frac{b}{c}\left(C_o + C_1\cos\theta + C_2\cos^2\theta\right)$$

TABLE XIX

ABSORPTION AND SCATTERING COEFFICIENTS DERIVED FROM RADIANCE
MEASUREMENTS
(After Lenoble, 1958a)

Region		Wavelength (nm)									
		330	335	344	354	360	368	378	390	404	413
Monaco	absorption coefficient (m^{-1})	0.13	0.12	0.10	0.08	0.07	0.06	0.05	0.04	0.03	0.03
	scattering coefficient (m^{-1})	0.10	0.09	0.09	0.07	0.08	0.08	0.08	0.08	0.07	0.07
Corse	absorption coefficient (m^{-1})	0.17	0.16	0.14	0.11	0.10	0.09	0.07	0.06	0.05	0.05
	scattering coefficient (m^{-1})	0.07	0.07	0.07	0.07	0.07	0.07	0.06	0.06	0.05	0.05

The physical meaning of radiance attenuation is directly evident
from his equations.

ASYMPTOTIC STATE

Radiance distribution

Some simple reasoning may help to understand how the radiance
distribution is modified with progressively increasing depth. It is
obvious that the complex structure predicted for the surface layer
will disappear when details in the distribution are smoothed out.
On account of the strong forward scattering, the distribution will be
concentrated around the direction of maximum radiance. Another
associated phase of the process would be an approach of the direction
of maximum radiance towards zenith because zenith radiance has the
shortest path and is therefore least attenuated. Consequently, the
change would lead to a distribution which is symmetrical round the
vertical.

WHITNEY (1941) conjectured from his observations of the underwater light field that with increase of depth the radiance distribution

would eventually settle down to a fixed form. The mathematical formulation of the final state has first been given by POOLE (1945) for the case of isotropic scattering. It is:

$$L(\theta) = \frac{1}{4\pi} \frac{b}{c} \frac{E_o}{1 + \dfrac{k}{c} \cos \theta} \tag{56}$$

where k is defined as the limit of the radiance attenuation coefficient K at great depths:

$$K = -\frac{1}{L} \cdot \frac{dL}{dz} \qquad \lim_{z \to \infty} K = k \tag{57}$$

The factor k is independent of direction, and always less than the attenuation coefficient c. In this case the asymptotic polar surface is a prolate ellipsoid with vertical axis and having eccentricity k/c. It is determined by inherent properties only, and irrespective of atmospheric lighting conditions and the state of the sea surface.

This model was substantially improved by LENOBLE (1956b) who introduced the specific scattering function (eq.55) and accordingly obtained better agreement between predicted and observed values of the irradiance ratios E_u/E_d and E_v/E_d. A mathematical proof of the existence of an asymptotic distribution is furnished by PREISENDORFER (1959). He discusses the asymptotic value, k, which is valid for deep waters when eq.49 takes the form:

$$L(\theta) = \frac{L_*(\theta)}{c + k \cos \theta} \tag{58}$$

It follows that the shape of all depth profiles of radiance will approach the asymptotic value k, i.e., radiance (and irradiance) attenuation is the same in all directions.

As established by eq.58, the ratio of the radiance to the path function is a parameter which denotes the members of a family of ellipses. TYLER (1963b) has shown that the measurable quantity $L(\theta)/L(90)$ can be fitted empirically to an ellipse through the relation:

$$\left(\frac{L(\theta)}{L(90)} \right)^{1/a} = \frac{1}{1 + \varepsilon \cos \theta} \tag{59}$$

where $\varepsilon = k/c$. Tyler tentatively puts $a = 4$, which fits with his near-asymptotic radiance data from Lake Pend Oreille.

Polarization

Conclusions about polarization in the sea can be drawn from our discussion of the polarization pattern generated by a beam of light (Chapter 2, p.42). On account of the symmetry of the asymptotic light field round the vertical, the corresponding asymptotic polarization state will show maximum polarization in the horizontal direction. TYLER (1963b) has simply assumed that the polarization resulting from scattering is described by the following equations:

$$L_H = \int L(\theta, \phi)(\cos^2 \theta + \sin^2 \theta \cos^2 \phi) d\omega$$

$$L_V = \int L(\theta, \phi)(\sin^2 \theta) d\omega$$

(60)

where $L(\theta, \phi)$ represents unpolarized radiance, L_H the horizontally polarized component and L_V the vertically polarized component, both for radiance in the horizontal direction. The degree of polarization is by definition:

$$p = \frac{L_H - L_V}{L_H + L_V}$$

Employing the model of eq.59, Tyler finds by integration of eq.60 that:

$$p = \varepsilon^2 = \frac{k^2}{c^2}$$

(61)

This conclusion results from a straightforward determination of the ratio of the asymptotic radiance attenuation coefficient to the total attenuation coefficient c.

The polarization of underwater radiance energy has also been the object of several theoretical studies by LENOBLE (1958b, 1961b, c), who employs eq.54 in its matrix form for diffuse radiant energy. Computations for Rayleigh scattering suggest that the degree of polarization in the asymptotic state is zero for zenith and for nadir radiance, and is maximum in the horizontal direction. This finding should hold true qualitatively for large particle scattering. Arguments given by TYLER (1963b) support this view, which is consistent with the observation of maximum radiance in the direction of the zenith.

CHAPTER 8

TECHNIQUES OF UNDERWATER LIGHT MEASUREMENT

From a physical point of view the measurement of radiant energy does not present any problems. The development of a simple and effective technique adapted for observation in the sea, however, has met with difficulties. There is no doubt that the work in this field has been hampered by technical inadequacies. Unfortunately, the pitfalls associated with radiance and irradiance measurements have not been known to all experimentalists, e.g., the occurrence of non-linearity in the relation between light flux and photocurrent and the devastating effect of the band-width error which occurs with broad colour filters. The advent of the photomultiplier tube has constituted a major break-through by making the use of interference filters possible. The technical means which form the basic units in the meters are discussed below with a view to pointing out the possibility of error in the measurements.

COLLECTORS

Radiance collectors

A Gershun tube (Fig.1) provides sufficient means of limiting the angle of acceptance so as to measure radiance as we have defined it. In the meter devised by DUNTLEY et al. (1955) and extensively used by TYLER (1960b), an internally baffled Gershun tube limits the angle to 6.6°. A lens-pinhole system (Fig.4) is often preferred, as it considerably reduces the length of the collector. There is not much to be gained by minimizing the angle of acceptance below about 6°; especially at angles near the solar direction where wave-induced fluctuations occur, an integration over a not too small solid angle is even to be recommended.

Irradiance collectors

The conventional design employs flat plate collectors, usually opal glass or opal plastic. These materials do not diffuse ideally and do not follow Lambert's cosine law strictly; in addition they possess some wavelength selectivity. The cosine error is not important when measuring downwelling flux, which is concentrated within the refraction cone of semi-angle 48.5°.

POOLE (1945) has pointed out that old measurements especially tend to undervalue the upward irradiance on account of poor functioning of the flat plate collector for relatively strong light with large angle of incidence (see also PELEVIN, 1966). An improvement in the performance of the collector is obtained by elevating its surface above the instrument case so that some light passes through the edge of the collector.

In some cases we aim at securing the magnitude of the total light, regardless of angle, received at a given point. This would, for instance, be best for assessing the energy available for photosynthesis. In this case a spherical (4π) collector which measures spherical

Fig.31. Meter for measuring spherical irradiance and attenuation coefficient in coastal waters. The collector is a hollow, translucent, white sphere at the top of the instrument. (After DUNTLEY, 1963.)

irradiance and thus scalar irradiance is ideal; it also has the advantage of being independent of the meter's orientation (Fig.31). In practice, however, a hemispherical (2π) collector seems to provide sufficient means to arrive at a representative value of the spherical irradiance since most light is within the refraction zone.

The measurement of scalar irradiance by means of a spherical collector represents equal collection. The ratio of equal collection to cosine collection for the upper hemisphere is defined by:

$$C = \frac{\int_0^{\frac{1}{2}\pi} \int_0^{2\pi} L(\theta, \phi, \zeta) \sin \theta \, d\theta \, d\phi}{\int_0^{\frac{1}{2}\pi} \int_0^{2\pi} L(\theta, \phi, \zeta) \sin \theta \cos \theta \, d\theta \, d\phi}$$

JERLOV and LILJEQUIST (1938) investigated the factor C for coastal waters and established its dependence on solar elevation, wavelength, turbidity and depth. For a low sun and very turbid water, C can attain a maximum value of 1.50. The lowest value of 1.10 appears with zenith sun and the clearest waters. Most frequently, one finds a factor of 1.20—1.30. A hemispherical collector reduces the variations in the factor C to a permissible level. The theory behind the spherical and hemispherical types of collectors is outlined by GERSHUN (1936).

For meters provided with a diffusing collector, it is obligatory to pay due regard to the so-called immersion effect (POOLE, 1936). This

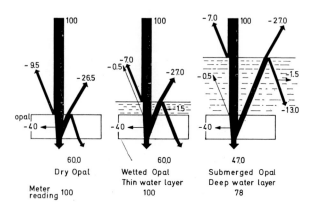

Fig.32. Reflection processes occurring for an opal glass used as cosine collector in irradiance meters. (After WESTLAKE, 1965.)

appears as a reduction in meter sensitivity when the meter is lowered from the surface to a small depth of the same order as the radius of the collector. The immersion effect is due largely to changes in reflection at the upper surface of the collector when the meter is submerged. Fig.32, prepared on the basis of calculations by BERGER (1961) and WESTLAKE (1965), gives a simplified illustration of the phenomenon. According to Berger the immersion effect is less for silicate glasses than for plastics, which have a relatively low refractive index. Since it may amount to 30 % and is dependent on the optical–geometrical design of the meter, this effect should be determined experimentally for each instrument.

DETECTORS

As regards flux-receiving detectors, a number of visual, photographic and photoelectric techniques are worth noting. KOZLYANINOV (1961) has visually compared the radiance in different directions and for different colours with daylight by using a shipboard tube, the lower end of which is submerged in the water.

Model experiments employing a spectrograph with photographic recording were made already in 1922 by KNUDSEN. The spectrophotographic method, though circumstantial, has the advantage of

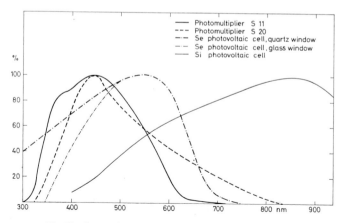

Fig.33. Spectral sensitivity of various photoelectric cells.

simultaneous measurements throughout the spectrum. It has been perfected for radiance observations by the French school (LE GRAND, 1939; LE GRAND et al., 1954; LENOBLE, 1956c; and IVANOFF, 1956). JERLOV and KOCZY (1951) were able to extend monochromatic irradiance measurements down to 500 m in the ocean by means of a unique photographic method.

The choice of photoelectric detectors is generally limited to a few devices only. In competition with other cells, the Se photovoltaic cell holds a central position for routine measurements of fairly strong light (Fig.33). A red-sensitive type is available having useful sensitivity well past 800 nm. A linear relationship between light flux and photocurrent exists only if the cell is exposed to less than 1,000 lux, i.e., 1.5 % of the brightest daylight, and only if the load resistance is low ($< 50 \, \Omega$) for the permissible upper light level. The temperature dependence of the Se cell is negligible for temperatures occurring in the sea.

The Si photovoltaic cell offers a favourable alternative for measurement in the red (Fig.33). As to linearity and temperature stability, it is comparable to the Se cell. When operated with a very high load resistance it has an almost logarithmic response.

It should be added that the advent of miniature, transistorized operational amplifiers, which can easily be built into the measuring head, opens new possibilities for using photovoltaic cells in an optimal way.

Measurements with the sensitive photomultiplier tube were initiated by SASAKI et al. (1955) and by CLARKE and WERTHEIM (1956). The use of this tube involves a far more complicated technique than does the photovoltaic cell. It requires a very well stabilized high voltage. Gain shift with time can be appreciable — 12% per day has been quoted — although in good tubes it can be as low as 0.5%—1% per day. The tube is usable only in weak light because of strong fatigue effects in the cathode, appreciable gain shift and temporary increase of dark current following large input signals.

The full advantages of the tube appear in records of low light levels. We should mention, however, the strong temperature dependence of the dark current (30 %/°C). A tube type with low inherent dark current should therefore be chosen, and it is definitely of value to incorporate a shutter in the meter in order to check the zero.

In conclusion, photomultiplier tubes should only be used in

applications when their superior sensitivity is really needed. Strong light is measured more accurately with the aid of photovoltaic cells.

Neutral filters should be selected on the basis of their ability to transmit virtually independently of the wavelength. Such filters, consisting of photographic negatives, are available, which reduce light to any desired level.

Colour filters are inserted between the collector and the detector. Without a collimator system, the light is partly transmitted obliquely through the colour filter. As a consequence, the effective thickness of the colour filter is greater than the geometric thickness. The notorious band-width error is due to a change in the width of the transmitted band and its position in the spectrum due to selective absorption by the water. JOSEPH (1949b) has presented an exhaustive analysis of the shift with depth of the optical centre λ_o of broad filters defined by:

$$\lambda_o(z) = \frac{\int \lambda E(\lambda, z) \cdot T(\lambda)S(\lambda)\mathrm{d}\lambda}{\int E(\lambda, z) \cdot T(\lambda)S(\lambda)\mathrm{d}\lambda}$$

where $S(\lambda)$ is the sensitivity of the detector, $T(\lambda)$ the transmittance of the filter. It may be seen from his results in Fig.34, representing several Schott filters used in the clearest ocean water, that only with the ultra-violet filter B12+U1 and the blue filter B12+G5 are the

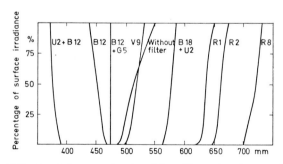

Fig.34. Shift of optical centre of various Schott filters when the meter is lowered. (After JOSEPH, 1949b.)

shifts small enough to guarantee high accuracy. Joseph further demonstrates that the current concept of a surface loss in irradiance measurements has arisen from observation impaired by band-width errors.

The problem of securing data for the red can be solved by forming a differential filter (SAUBERER and RUTTNER, 1941). If, for instance, the readings with R2 are deducted from those with R1 the error is reduced to a permissible level. In turbid green waters the filter V9 (4 mm) is suitable, whereas the performance of the ultra violet-filter is inadequate.

The band-width error is insignificant for interference filters of narrow band widths. TYLER (1959) has pointed out that light leakage may appear outside the stated filter band even if secondary transmission peaks are eliminated. When measuring in the red, an infinitesimal leakage in the blue will introduce an enormous error which becomes progressively larger as the depth increases. This treacherous error must be eliminated by employing suitable blocking filters. The performance of interference filters requires low convergence of the incident beam. LISSBERGER and WILCOCK (1959) have proved, however, that the deterioration which appears as a displacement of the maximum wavelength towards shorter wavelengths and as an increase in the width of the passband is small even at a convergence of semi-angle 10°. Interference filters have also been successfully used in conjunction with a photovoltaic cell for irradiance measurements in the surface strata (IVANOFF et al., 1961).

ORIENTATION PROBLEM

The in situ orientation of irradiance meters presents no special difficulties. It should be stressed, however, that an oblique (not vertical) cable often entails angular deviation of a flat plate collector. This may be corrected by mounting the meter on gimbals.

The setting of radiance meters at defined directions in the sea is a matter of crucial importance. It may be assumed a priori that with a clear sun maximum radiance in all horizontal planes occurs in the azimuth of the sun, which thus serves as reference direction. By rotating the meter around a vertical axis, representative records for all azimuths can be obtained. The securing of accurate vertical angles

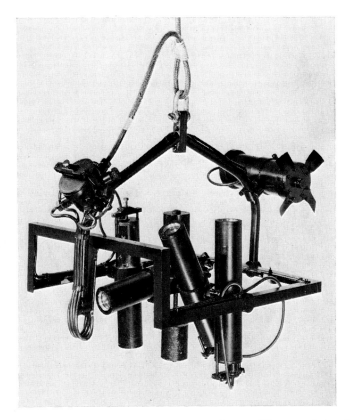

Fig.35. Radiance meters with four measuring heads set at different vertical angles and mounted on gimbals. The whole assembly is turned round a vertical axis by means of a motor.

is more critical. Only in shallow depths and with a heavy meter can one be assured that the vertical angle is unaffected by the drift of the ship or the drag of prevailing currents. For measurements at greater depths a reference direction is necessary. A simple solution to this problem, which utilizes the gimbals principle, is afforded by the arrangement shown in Fig.35. The four measuring heads mounted on gimbals can be set at different vertical angles. The assembly is unaffected by the movements of the meter provided that the units present equal torque section to currents above and below the pivots.

METERS

Radiance meters

The principal function of the radiance meter is clear from the preceding discussion. Various technical solutions to the problem of exploring the light field have been given. The instrument of DUNTLEY et al. (1955) scans continuously in the vertical plane from zenith to nadir; the azimuth position is controlled by means of a servo-system in combination with a propeller to rotate the meter. The meter, designed by SASAKI et al. (1962b), is stabilized with a large fin and has two measuring heads which, by means of synchronous motors, scan in the horizontal plane and in different vertical planes respectively (Fig.36). TIMOFEEVA (1962) uses a spherical container in which the receiving system is installed. It can be smoothly and reversibly

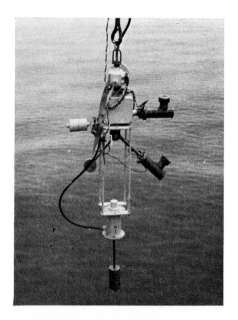

Fig.36. Radiance meter stabilized with a large fin and with two measuring heads which, by means of synchronous motors, scan in the horizontal plane and in different vertical planes. (After SASAKI et al., 1962b.)

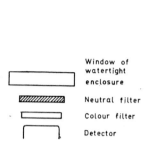

Fig.37. Outline of basic arrangement in an irradiance meter.

turned around a vertical axis and discontinuously every 10° (within certain limits) around a horizontal axis.

On the spectrophotometric side we have to note the designs given by the French school (see LENOBLE, 1958a). These meters are well adapted to underwater use and are especially suitable in the ultra-violet region.

Irradiance meters

An outline of the basic arrangement in an irradiance meter is exhibited in Fig.37. The proper use of the photovoltaic cell is demonstrated in a model of high versatility devised by HOLMES and SNODGRASS (1961). A meter of advanced technique has been designed by BODEN et al. (1960). This is a telerecording instrument with a photomultiplier tube which gives a logarithmic response over seven decades of irradiance. The anode current is kept constant by varying automatically the high voltage which in turn is used as a measure of the light flux. Interference filters are automatically changed, and an electrically operated shutter selects one of three positions, namely open, closed or pinhole.

A multicore cable is well suited for meters which record in the upper strata, 0—200 m; a telemetering system is not needed in this case. It is worthwhile paying scrupulous attention to the light leakage problem in the meters. At deep levels the blue light is strongly dominant, and as little as two-fold reflection of this light against the

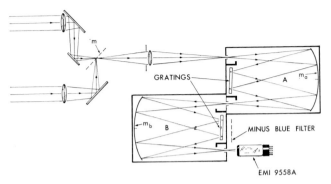

Fig.38. Optical system of the Scripps spectroradiometer. (TYLER and SMITH, 1966.)

blackened interior of the meter may be critical. JERLOV (1965) has built an irradiance meter which is provided with an effective light screen for the multiplier tube in order to eliminate the effect of stray light.

HUBBARD (1958) has described a prism spectrophotometer which, when operated in combination with a recorder on deck, presents measurements of irradiance or radiance as a function of wavelength; the optical system sweeps the range from 400 to 600 nm with a band width of about 10 nm. The spectroradiometer, carefully tested and calibrated by TYLER and SMITH (1966), is essentially a double Ebert monochromator with a double objective system which allows of measurements relative to a standard source (Fig.38). Great precautions have been taken to reduce stray light within the instrument. The wavelength setting can be changed in 5 nm steps by remote control.

It is desirable in biological productivity studies to use integrating recorders. Adequate techniques for integrating irradiance over prolonged periods of time have been described by SNODGRASS (1961) and by CURRIE and DRAPER (1961).

Polarimeters

Like radiance meters, in situ polarimeters must be designed to permit measurements in different directions. As to methods, one encounters the usual display of visual, photographic and photoelectric techniques. The initial observations by WATERMAN (1955) were made with a special polarization analyser, which, when traversed by convergent polarized light, forms an interference pattern; this is then photographed and the figures are contrast-evaluated. Visual methods may be employed for quantitative observations down to depths accessible by divers. The extension to greater depths demands polarimeters with remote control. The meter designed by IVANOFF (1957b) is composed of a revolving polaroid filter acting as an analyser and a photovoltaic cell in combination with a filter-changing device. It allows scanning in a horizontal direction down to a depth of 120 m. Ample opportunities for studying polarization with a photoelectric as well as with a photographic technique were afforded by dives with the underwater chamber "Kuroshio" (SASAKI et al., 1959). The meter used by TIMOFEEVA (1962) is the radiance meter described, provided with a slowly revolving polaroid analyser in front of the phototube.

CALIBRATION

Meters are calibrated in absolute units by means of an artificial light source of known spectral emission, e.g., a high pressure Xe lamp, a tungsten band lamp or an iodine lamp. The spectral distribution of radiant energy from the sun can be simulated by a tungsten lamp in combination with Davis and Gibson liquid filters. Another method, elaborated by JERLOV and OLSSON (1944), employs the strong flux from the sun in the standardization procedure.

It is necessary to check the response of the detectors for linearity in the actual range of measurement. The temperature effect of photovoltaic cells for temperature variations occurring in the sea is negligible, but it cannot be disregarded for photomultiplier tubes.

MEASURING PROCEDURE

Field work will be briefly commented upon. Needless to say, weather conditions place severe restrictions on underwater light observations, which require fairly constant lighting conditions above the sea. Under clear skies the meter should be freely exposed to the sun without being appreciably affected by light reflected from the ship side. Owing to pitching motions of the ship, the meter cannot be lowered (from a beam) more than 5–7 m outboard, and therefore shading due to the ship may influence the results. POOLE (1936) has considered the shading error and estimated its magnitude at about 10 % in the uppermost 5 m for diffuse light; it is of no practical importance for bright sunlight.

Readings should be taken in quick succession when the meter is lowered, as this tends to impede the development of cable obliquity. A depth-sensing unit facilitates accurate depth determinations. Deck photometers mounted on gimbals and freely exposed serve to record fluctuations in the light over water. It should be borne in mind that these are not always closely correlated to the variations of the light field at great depths. Observations with a cloud-shielded sun are made under drastically altered lighting conditions, and cannot be compared with those for a clear sun.

CHAPTER 9

RADIANCE

RADIANCE IN THE UPPER LAYERS

Observed radiance distributions

It is clear from the preceding discussion that the radiance distribution near the surface is rather complex due to the effects of refraction and reflexion at the air–water interface. Available observations also reveal the fine details in the angular structure of radiance. Some typical examples are shown in Fig.39 for clear weather (JERLOV and FUKUDA, 1960), hazy weather (SASAKI et al., 1962b) and overcast sky (TYLER, 1958). The fact is established that the angular dependence of radiance observed in turbid water for clear skies agrees reasonably well with the trends predicted by the simple theory (Chapter 7, p.84), which considers radiance as an integration of skylight and of light generated by primary scattering. Discrepancies between the theoretical and the experimental picture may be attributed to the effect of wave motion which is apt to smooth fine details in the theoretical pattern derived for a flat surface. The weak maximum computed for 150° does not show up in Fig.39 because of lack of sufficiently dense observations in this region.

The distributions in Fig.39 bear witness to the strong radiance maximum in the apparent direction of the sun. The structure in the neighbourhood of this direction has also been studied by IVANOFF and MOREUIL (1963) who found that in clear and calm weather the radiance at 50 m in the Mediterranean is reduced to half of its value at ± 5° from the sun and to a quarter of it at ± 10°. As pointed out in Chapter 6, the angle subtended by the refracted glitter expands with increasing wave action. For even moderate winds it is larger than the acceptance angles of the radiance meters described, and therefore the glitter cannot be comprehended by a single radiance value.

The sets of radiance curves in Fig.39 clearly exhibit the conspicu-

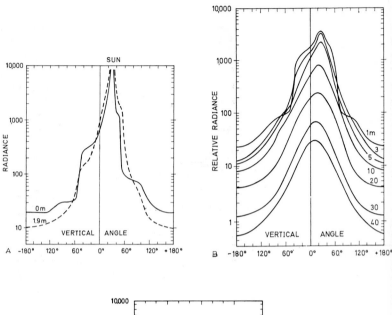

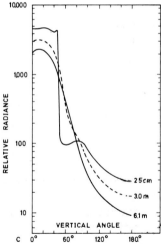

Fig.39. Radiance distribution in the vertical plane of the sun for relatively turbid water. A. Clear day, Gullmar Fjord, 535 nm (after JERLOV and FUKUDA, 1960). B. Hazy weather, off Japan, 520 nm (after SASAKI et al., 1962b). C. Overcast sky, Lake Pend Oreille, 480 nm (after TYLER, 1958).

ous fall of the curve at the edge of the refraction cone ($\pm$ 48.5°) as well as the distinct peaks at 90° formed by light from below which has been totally reflected at the surface.

It is a primary trend of radiance measurements that with increasing

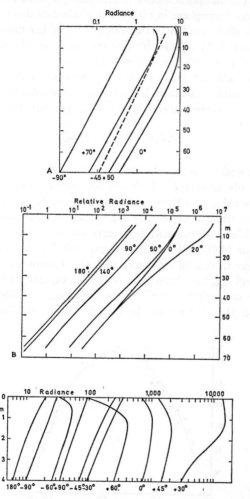

Fig.40. Depth profiles of radiance for different zenith angles in the plane of the sun on a clear day. A. After TIMOFEEVA (1951a). B. Lake Pend Oreille (after TYLER, 1960b). C. Gullmar Fjord (after JERLOV and FUKUDA, 1960).

depth the distribution becomes less directed and more diffuse. It is clear from the distributions of high resolution in Fig.39 that the fine structure is gradually extinguished and that the peaks at $\pm\,90°$ disappear rapidly towards greater depth as predicted by the theory.

The spectacular phenomenon that radiance in some angular ranges of the upper hemisphere in turbid water increases down to a certain depth was discovered by TIMOFEEVA (1951a). Comparative results are presented in Fig.40. In this case the experimental and theoretical sides supplement each other. In weakly scattering water, real maxima in radiance are not likely to develop because of the presence of skylight of higher radiance. Logarithmic curves obtained by MOREL (1965) for the Mediterranean exhibit some curvature but no maxima.

Zenith and nadir radiance

A great deal of the experimental radiance material concerns studies of the zenith radiance L_0. It should be observed with regard to the above discussion that the interpretation of the depth dependence of L_0 is intimately connected with the scattering mechanism. IVANOFF (1956, 1957a) has evaluated L_0 spectra and shown that the spectral distribution (400—650 nm) is changed with increase of depth in a way similar to that of irradiance (Fig.41). Comparative studies of L_0, L_{90} and L_{180} have been made by LE GRAND and LENOBLE (1955), and by LENOBLE (1956c, 1957b, 1958a). By numerous observations in the region 318—413 nm off the French Atlantic and Mediterranean

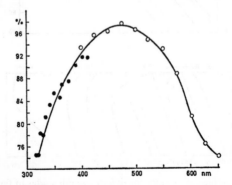

Fig.41. Transmittance per meter of zenith radiance off Corsica for the ultraviolet region (after LENOBLE, 1958a) and for the visible region (after IVANOFF, 1957a).

coasts, Lenoble has laid a firm basis for our knowledge of the ultra-violet field. One example of spectral zenith radiance is adduced in Fig.41. Lenoble's theoretical analysis decomposes the radiance attenuation coefficient K into an absorption coefficient and a scattering coefficient and represents these properties as spectral functions (Table XIX).

The behaviour of the radiance L_{180} with change of depth generally follows the simple law of eq.41. Its spectral composition is similar to that of upward irradiance and will be treated in Chapter 10.

ASYMPTOTIC RADIANCE DISTRIBUTION

Approach to the asymptotic state

The broad outlines of the change of the light field with depth were explored in the first measurements (JERLOV and LILJEQUIST, 1938; WHITNEY, 1941). The surface radiance curves, which are sharply peaked in the apparent direction of the sun, are gradually transformed into distributions of less directed character as the depth increases; the attenuation is maximum for angles near the solar direction. The process by which the approach to an asymptotic distribution takes place through the combined effects of absorption and scattering is illustrated in the curves of Fig.39 and 42 obtained for different localities. TYLER's (1960b) results for radiance through eighteen vertical angles and ten azimuth angles collected under favourable experimental conditions in the uniform water of Lake Pend Oreille present data of unparalleled accuracy. Actually, there is no reason to believe that scattering in lake water would differ appreciably from that in sea water.

TIMOFEEVA (1951a) has demonstrated experimentally that the logarithmic curves for different angles at increasingly greater depths tend to straight lines parallel to each other, thereby providing powerful support for the theory. In consequence the attenuation coefficient reaches an asymptotic value, valid for all directions, which is the theoretical k-value (eq.58).

TYLER (1960a) has formulated the general principle in the attenuation as follows: "Radiances with magnitudes that are relatively too large to conform with the asymptotic radiance distribution are

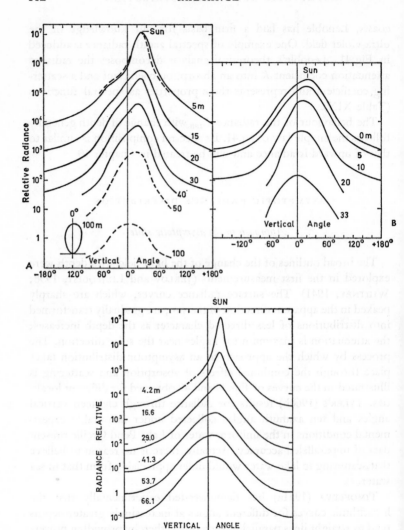

Fig.42. Change with increase of depth of radiance in the vertical plane of the sun towards the asymptotic state. A. Baltic Sea, green light (continuous line, after JERLOV and LILJEQUIST, 1938; dashed line after measurements by N. Jerlov and K. Nygård). B. Gullmar Fjord, blue light. C. Lake Pend Oreille, green light (after TYLER, 1960b).

attenuated rapidly whereas those with magnitudes that are relatively too small are attenuated slowly, or even enhanced. The net effect of this process is to inexorably return the distribution to its asymptotic shape. It follows that there must be a value of radiance which will be attenuated linearly over all depths. Its magnitude will depend on the values of c and b — —."

DUNTLEY (1963) has pointed out that the shape of the radiance distribution in Tyler's family of curves has almost reached its asymptotic form at 41 m depth whereas the peak of the curve is not at zenith but is rather, at this depth, shifting at a maximum rate. This feature is corroborated by other results in Fig.42. By extrapolation, Duntley has found that the true asymptotic radiance (546 nm) distribution in Lake Pend Oreille is not reached until 100 m depth.

In the marine environment the transfer to an asymptotic state progresses more slowly. The change of the light field is not yet completed at 100 m for the residual green light in the Baltic, and at 400 m for blue light in the Sargasso Sea (Fig.43). The comparison demonstrates a slight difference in shape between turbid and clear water.

In the trivial case of zenith sun, strict symmetry around the vertical exists for all levels and an analogous transformation to a final shape takes place. An overcast sky also presents a symmetrical distribution, and the asymptotic state is evidently reached close to the surface as evidenced by TAKENOUTI (1940), WHITNEY (1941) and LENOBLE (1957a) (Fig.44).

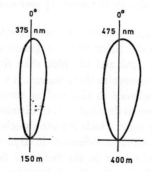

Fig.43. Polar diagram of near-asymptotic radiance distribution in the Sargasso Sea. Solar elevation 60°.

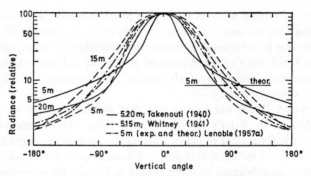

Fig.44. Symmetrical radiance distribution, independent of azimuthal angle for an overcast sky.

Asymptotic distribution and solar elevation

Certain aspects of the asymptotic distribution remain unclear. For instance, the dependence of radiance magnitude on the solar altitude has not been investigated in sufficient detail. Only SASAKI et al. (1958c) have furnished some values of L_{90} for different altitudes at 5 m and 10 m depth. Their pseudo-elliptical diagrams display maximum distension at 23° altitude. TYLER (1961b) has attributed this maximum as the product of two superposed effects, namely scattering from sunlight, which increases with angle of incidence in the horizontal plane, and reflection at the surface, which reduces transmitted flux when the sun sets.

Asymptotic distribution for different wavelengths

It is plainly brought out in the investigation of JERLOV and LILJEQUIST (1938) in the Baltic that the directionality in radiance is more marked for the red and the blue than for the green, which shows minimum attenuance in these waters. It is consistent with the general picture of radiance as outlined by theory and experiments that the transformation to the final state of distribution is most slowly accomplished for the light which is least absorbed. Thus it is noted in Fig.43 that a considerable difference in asymptotic depth occurs for the violet and the blue in the Sargasso Sea. The asymptotic distribution for 700 nm prevails at less than 50 m depth in all natural waters.

CHAPTER 10

IRRADIANCE

The study of the selective attenuation of irradiance in the upper layers of the sea is one of the primary objects of optical oceanography. There is a remarkable and unfortunate paucity of experimental work on irradiance. Most data result from sporadic observations without or with one colour filter having a broad band width; systematic and complete spectral measurements of irradiance are sparse. The explanation of this lack of relevant information for vast oceanic areas is to be found not only in the technical difficulties stated but also in bad weather conditions, since the measurements require fairly stable atmospheric lighting conditions and not too rough sea.

DOWNWARD IRRADIANCE IN THE UPPER LAYERS

Survey of observations in the visible

We cannot go into particulars about measurements with broad filters. In Fig.45 and 52, spectral curves of downward irradiance E_d for different depths are given which represent corrected data obtained with broad band filters and data obtained with interference filters. The spectral distribution of irradiance shows a maximum at 480—500 nm at the surface. With increasing depth, the peak shifts slowly towards 465 nm in clear ocean water (east Mediterranean). A salient asymmetry of the spectral curve develops as the violet becomes stronger than the green. A slightly higher turbidity, such as occurs in the Caribbean Sea, extinguishes the asymmetry and brings about a symmetrical form of the distribution curve. Overall decreased irradiance transmittance reduces the shortwave part of the spectrum more than the longwave part and shifts the maximum of transmittance toward longer wavelengths because of selective absorption by particles and yellow substance. This general principle is confirmed

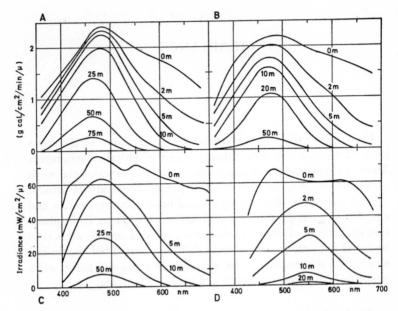

Fig.45. Spectral distributions of downward irradiance for high solar elevations. A. Eastern Mediterranean. B. Caribbean Sea (after JERLOV, 1951). C. Off Japan (after SASAKI et al., 1958a). D. Baltic Sea (after AHLQUIST, 1965).

by NEUYMIN et al. (1964) for north Atlantic waters. The Baltic Sea, which is abundant in yellow substance, displays maximum shift of the transmittance peak (to 550 nm), while the ultra-violet of 375 nm is extinguished even at 5 m.

Another set of curves represents on a logarithmic scale the percentage of irradiance compared to surface irradiance as a function of depth (Fig. 46). The presence of a curvature, which is most obvious for the blue and the violet, is a consequence of the change with depth of the radiance of scattered light (Chapter 9) and is defined by integration of this radiance. The strongest curvature is in clear water at 50 m for 475 nm. With increase of turbidity, it ascends and becomes less conspicuous.

Observations in the ultra-violet

There is every reason to treat observations of the far ultra-violet

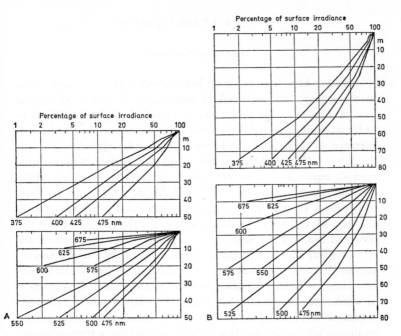

Fig.46. Depth profiles of downward irradiance (cf. Fig.45) in percent of surface irradiance. A. Caribbean Sea. B. East Mediterranean.

in this connection even if they are obtained by a somewhat different technique. In 1947 JERLOV found that the transmittance of radiant energy of 310 nm in clear water exhibits maximum values of 86 %/m, which is by far more than previously found. This kind of energy is strongly influenced by absorption due to particles and yellow substance. The span of transmittance fluctuation is therefore large; in the tropical part of the ocean it is from 50 to 80 %/m. In a coastal area such as the Skagerrak the maximum value does not exceed 10 % /m. The optical properties in the far ultra-violet thus undergo a drastic change from oceanic to coastal water types.

OPTICAL CLASSIFICATION

Basis of classification

Attempts have been made to bring about some systematic order in the experimental material of irradiance. A scheme of optical classification of ocean water was propounded by JERLOV (1951) in order to distinguish different water types in terms of spectral transmittance of downward irradiance at high solar altitudes. By synthesizing available observational data from surface waters, three normal transmittance curves were obtained representing three different optical water types, *I*, *II* and *III*. Several factors combine to permit a simple description of the attenuation process and its change with turbidity. An essential basis for the classification is the observed fact that the shape of the volume scattering function for surface water shows only small variations from one oceanic area to another. It has been demonstrated that particulate material and yellow substance are primary agencies for selective absorption. A connection between these two parameters exists in so far as yellow substance originates from decaying particles. The relationship between the irradiance attenuation coefficient (465 nm) and the scattering coefficient *b*, both given as mean values in the water column 0—50 m, is more closely interpreted in Fig.47. The limiting curve represents

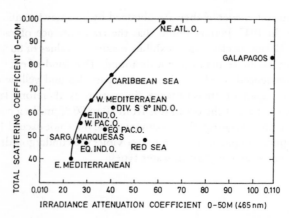

Fig.47. Comparison for oceanic stations of downward irradiance attenuation coefficient (465 nm) and scattering coefficient. (After JERLOV, 1951.)

the lowest attenuance for a given particle scattering. Some regions fall significantly off this curve. Except for the Red Sea, which also contains a red or yellow component, these are upwelling areas off the west coasts of continents and regions of divergence. The deviations of these productive areas are generally attributed to selective absorption by yellow substance and particles. They are also an effect of the larger particle size in nutrient-rich water than in less fertile water, the larger size tending to diminish the ratio of scatterance to absorption. It may be concluded that the distribution of particles and yellow substance, and ultimately of irradiance attenuance, is controlled by those dynamical processes in the sea which have an important bearing on productivity. The observed irradiances form a pattern which in broad outlines corresponds to the general oceanic circulation (see Fig.50), with minima in the upwelling regions and maxima in the nutrient-poor areas of the eastern Mediterranean and the Sargasso Sea.

Optical water types

As a considerable number of oceanic spectral transmittances fall between the two basic types *I* and *II*, a subdivision is called for. Therefore two intermediate types, *IA* and *IB*, are added (JERLOV, 1964). Most of the available irradiance values extracted from data

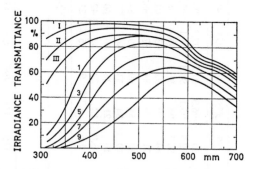

Fig.48. Transmittance per meter of downward irradiance in the surface layer for optical water types. Oceanic types *I, II, III* and coastal types *1, 3, 5, 7, 9*.

found in the literature are incorporated in the five spectral transmittance distributions given in Table XX and Fig.48.

TABLE XX

IRRADIANCE TRANSMITTANCE FOR SURFACE WATER OF DIFFERENT WATER TYPES

Irradiance transmittance (%/m)

Water type	Wavelength (nm)															
	310	350	375	400	425	450	475	500	525	550	575	600	625	650	675	700
I	86	94	96.3	97.2	97.8	98.1	98.2	97.2	96.1	94.2	92	85	74	70	66	59
IA	83	92.5	95.1	96.3	97.1	97.4	97.5	96.6	95.5	93.6	91	84	73.5	69.5	65.5	58.5
IB	80	90.5	94	95.5	96.4	96.7	96.8	96.0	95.0	93.0	90.5	83	73	69	65	58.0
II	69	84	89	92	93.5	94	94	93.5	92.5	90.5	87.5	80	71	67.5	63.5	56
III	50	71	79	84	87	88.5	89	89	88.5	86.5	82.5	75	68	65	61	54
1	16	32	54	69	79	84	87.5	88.8	88.5	86.5	82.5	75	68	65	61	54
3	9	19	34	53	66	75	80	82	82	81	78	71	65	62	57	51
5	3	10	21	36	50	60	67	71	73	72	70	67	62	58	52	45
7		5.0	12	22	32	42	50	56	61	63	63	62	58	53	46	40
9		1.5	4.7	9	15	21	29	37	46	53	56	55	52	47	40	33

Irradiance transmittance (%/10 m)

Water type	Wavelength (nm)															
	310	350	375	400	425	450	475	500	525	550	575	600	625	650	675	700
I	22	54	69	75	80	82.5	83.5	75	67	55	43	20	4.9	2.8	1.6	0.5
IA	16	45	60.5	68.5	74.5	77	78	71	63	52	39	17	4.6	2.6	1.4	0.5
IB	11	37	54	63	69	71.5	72	66.5	60	48	37	15	4.3	2.4	1.3	0.4
II	2	18	31	43	51	54	54	51	46	37	26	11	3.5	1.9	1.0	0.3

TABLE XXI

PERCENTAGE OF TOTAL IRRADIANCE (300–2,500 nm) FROM SUN AND SKY[1]

Depth (m)	Oceanic water					Coastal water				
	I	IA	IB	II	III	1	3	5	7	9
0	100	100	100	100	100	100	100	100	100	100
1	44.5	44.1	42.9	42.0	39.4	36.9	33.0	27.8	22.6	17.6
2	38.5	37.9	36.0	34.7	30.3	27.1	22.5	16.4	11.3	7.5
5	30.2	29.0	25.8	23.4	16.8	14.2	9.3	4.6	2.1	1.0
10	22.2	20.8	16.9	14.2	7.6	5.9	2.7	0.69	0.17	0.052
20						1.3	0.29	0.020		
25	13.2	11.1	7.7	4.2	0.97					
50	5.3	3.3	1.8	0.70	0.041	0.022				
75	1.68	0.95	0.42	0.124	0.0018					
100	0.53	0.28	0.10	0.0228						
150	0.056			0.00080						
200	0.0062									

[1] For oceanic water the solar altitude is 90°; for coastal water 45°.

An extension of the classification to greater depths — preferably to the lower limit of the photic zone — greatly improves its usefulness. An argument against this would be the optical nonuniformity of the water, for instance due to particle accumulation often encountered near the thermocline (KOZLYANINOV, 1959; BODEN et al., 1960). Such irregularities cause fairly small discrepancies and are not destructive of classification. The derived logarithmic curves for the whole family of water types are exhibited in Fig.49 for blue light (465 nm) only.

There is a need to broaden the basis for the classification. Most irradiance data fit well on the set of transmittance curves, but this does not exclude the possibility that significant deviations may be detected. For example, there are instances of Sargasso water being more transparent than type *I*. There is also evidence that coastal waters which contain a variable amount of terrigeneous material show divergent behaviour in the shortwave part of the spectrum. The coastal types *1–9* in Table XX and Fig.48 are derived from observa-

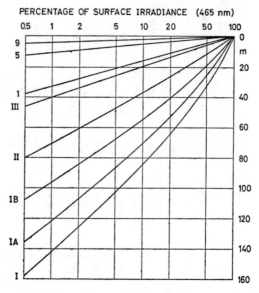

Fig.49. Depth profiles of downward irradiance in percent of surface radiance for defined optical water types. Oceanic types *I, IA, IB, II, III* and coastal types *1, 5, 9.*

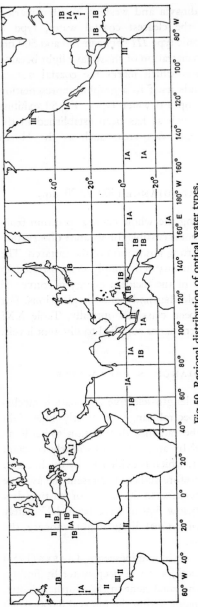

Fig.50. Regional distribution of optical water types.

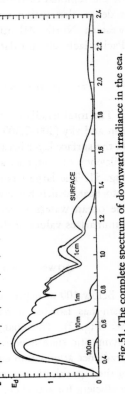

Fig.51. The complete spectrum of downward irradiance in the sea.

tion along the coasts of Scandinavia and western North America. The transmittance curve for the clearest coastal water, type *1*, coincides with that for the oceanic type *III* between 700 and 500 nm but tends toward much lower penetration of shortwave light because of the high selective absorption which marks the coastal waters.

The oceanic classification lends itself to a graphic representation of the regional distribution of optical water types. Fig.50 exhibits a dense observation net, e.g., such as has been established in the western North Atlantic, whereas vast areas such as the North Pacific lack relevant data.

TOTAL DOWNWARD IRRADIANCE (300–2,500 nm)

The total irradiance comprising the whole energy spectrum from sun and sky (300–2,500 nm) is not accessible for accurate observation in the surface layer because of strong absorption of the infrared. The efficiency of water as a monochromator is amply demonstrated in Fig. 51. The largest part by far of the incident energy is converted into heat, which has considerable thermodynamic implications. For the ocean waters which have been classified optically, Table XXI summarizes values of the total irradiance supplied to different levels.

DOWNWARD IRRADIANCE IN DEEP WATER

Below 100 m depth, the wavelength-selective attenuation mechanism has isolated a narrow spectral range of mostly blue light (see Fig.52). The change of the radiance distribution towards an asymptotic state is accompanied by an approach to nearly constant irradiance attenuation coefficient, which is evidenced by the linearity of the logarithmic curves. It therefore suffices to present the average coefficient for actual depth intervals, as in the survey of existing data in Table XXII. Here, depths below 500 m have been deliberately omitted since a background of animal light might enhance the ambient irradiance at these levels.

In connection with his studies on bioluminescence, CLARKE (1933) has contributed greatly to the exploration of deep water by finding a minimum value of 0.025 for the coefficient in the North Atlantic. For the rest, the coefficient remains within the interval 0.030–0.040

TABLE XXII

MEASUREMENTS OF IRRADIANCE ATTENUATION COEFFICIENTS AT DEEP LEVELS IN CLEAR WEATHER

Area	Depth range (m)	Attenuation coefficient (m^{-1})	Reference
Off Tahiti	100—400	0.034	JERLOV and KOCZY (1951)
Sargasso Sea	100—400	0.040	
	400—500	0.038	
Florida Current	160—460	0.034	CLARKE and WERTHEIM (1956)
	460—580	0.038	
Slope Water off	92—400	0.039	
New York	400—554	0.032	
Bay of Biscay	98—350	0.038	BODEN et al. (1960)
	300—405	0.033	
Off Californian coast	200—350	0.040[1]	KAMPA (1961)
Off Bermuda	200—550	0.030[1]	
Golfe du Lion	200—400	0.035[1]	
Off Madeira	200—400	0.032	JERLOV and NYGÅRD (1961)
	400—530	0.035	
West Indian Ocean	200—800	0.022—0.033	CLARKE and KELLY (1964)
North Atlantic			
41° 26′ N 55° 46′ W	100—350	0.031	CLARKE and KELLY (1965)
47° 27′ N 40° 50′ W	250—750	0.023	
46° 45′ N 35° 33′ W	75—300	0.030	

[1] Computed by N. G. Jerlov.

with one significant exception. This is the only experiment conducted up to now in an upwelling zone, namely off the Californian Coast (KAMPA, 1961). The high value of 0.058 found in this case suggests that selective absorption plays an important role down to 350 m.

IRRADIANCE ON A VERTICAL PLANE

The irradiance on a vertical plane, i.e., the horizontal irradiance component E_h, has attracted some attention because the ratio E_h/E_d

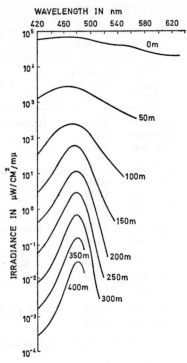

Fig.52. Spectral distribution of downward irradiance in Golfe du Lion. (After KAMPA, 1961.)

(E_d = the downward irradiance) is recognized as an indicator of the obliquity of the underwater light. By means of a cubical photometer, this ratio was accurately measured by ATKINS and POOLE (1940, 1958). The information that may be extracted from their observations indicates that the actual ratio E_h/E_d varies from 75 to 85 % and that it attains a constant value with increasing depth. Data obtained by JERLOV and KOCZY (1951) suggest a value of 60 % at 400 m in the Sargasso Sea. These findings are in general agreement with the structure of the radiance distribution. This can be verified from TYLER and SHAULES' (1964) integration of radiance, which yields irradiance on planes of different vertical and azimuthal angles.

UPWARD IRRADIANCE

The upward irradiance E_u, i.e., the irradiance falling on a horizontal surface facing downwards, is a subject which has attracted great interest. This component is readily observed, since it fluctuates much less because of wave action than does the downward light.

KALLE (1939b) anticipated that the spectral distribution curve for E_u would be peaked at a wavelength smaller than the 465 nm observed for E_d. The shift is attributed to highly wavelength-selective molecular scattering which occurs to some degree as multiple scattering. The experimental proof was given by JERLOV (1951) (Fig.53). Other confirmatory data are furnished by observations from shipboard or from aircraft (IVANOFF et al., 1961; STAMM and LANGEL, 1961; KOZLYANINOV and SEMENCHENKO, 1962; DUNTLEY, 1963).

Thus upward irradiance exhibits experimental distribution curves of quite different shape than does downward irradiance. It is interesting to note that JOSEPH (1950) deduced a distribution curve for pure water which is peaked at 460 nm. KOZLYANINOV (1960) found

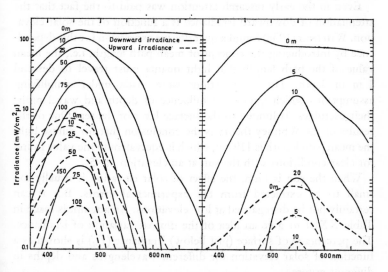

Fig.53. Comparison between spectral distribution of downward and upward irradiance for solar elevation of 55—60°. Left: Sargasso Sea ("Dana" expedition, 1966). Right: Baltic Sea (after AHLQUIST, 1965).

that the maximum at 80 m remains at 450 nm. The set of curves in Fig. 53, on the other hand, indicate a slight shift toward larger wavelengths with increase of depth. It is logical to assume that the maximum in the spectral distribution of E_u will, at great depths, occur at the wavelength of the residual light, namely 465 nm.

The relatively high irradiance ratio E_u/E_d of 6 % in the blue caused for the most part by molecular scattering is characteristic of the clearest waters. In this case the red back-scattering chiefly due to particles, is extremely low. In turbid ocean water the molecular scattering is of no importance; the ratio E_u/E_d is considerably lower and becomes maximum (2–3 %) for the most penetrating wavelength. In the red, this ratio is relatively higher in turbid water than in clear water (Fig.53).

DEPENDENCE OF IRRADIANCE ON SOLAR ELEVATION

Downward irradiance

Even in the early research attention was paid to the fact that the attenuation of downward irradiance is a function of the solar elevation. WHITNEY (1938) found a quantitative expression for this dependence by introducing the concept of mean path length, i.e., the mean value of the path length that light quanta must travel to descend 1 m in depth. His computations were made under simplifying assumptions which ignore the influence of depth and wavelength; their usefulness is limited to the surface layer of the sea. One of the results of the Whitney theory is the conclusion that for diffuse light the mean path length is 119 cm, which is equivalent to the value found for clear conditions with the sun at an elevation of 45°.

When the sun is high, the effect of solar elevation is usually too small to be extracted from the experimental errors. But it can certainly not be disregarded at low elevations. An attempt is made in Table XXIII to give an idea of the diurnal variation of irradiance. The percentage of surface (just below) irradiance (E_d) is shown as a function of solar elevation for different wavelengths and depths in different waters.

It may be seen from eq.39 that the solar elevation effect in surface water increases with the attenuation coefficient c. Minimum depend-

TABLE XXIII

PERCENTAGE OF SURFACE DOWNWARD IRRADIANCE FOR DIFFERENT SOLAR
ELEVATIONS

Region	Depth (m)	Solar altitude (°)	Wavelength (nm)					
			375	450	484	550	574	600
Sargasso Sea	10	30	55		70		21	
("Dana" expedition, 1966)		50	61		78		29	
	50	30	8.9		17		0.2	
		50	13.5		32		0.4	
Baltic Sea	10	10		0.48		7.1		2.3
(From AHLQUIST's		20		0.68		9.2		2.8
measurements,		30		0.97		11.7		3.3
1965)		40		1.40		15.0		4.0
		50		2.00		19.3		4.8
		60		2.80		24.6		5.8
	20	10		0.009		0.67		0.11
		20		0.014		0.88		0.14
		30		0.020		1.16		0.18
		40		0.029		1.52		0.24
		50		0.043		2.00		0.30
		60		0.064		2.62		0.38

ence in clear water should occur for the most penetrating blue light. The effect ceases to exist in the asymptotic state for which irradiance attenuance is constant regardless of solar elevation. Since the asymptotic radiance distribution is encountered at different depths for different wavelengths, the whole problem becomes rather complex. It is clear from theory and experiment (Table XXIV) that the solar elevation effect is much more influenced by wavelength for irradiance than for irradiance attenuation coefficient $d(\ln E_a)/dz$.

As long as sunlight dominates in the global light, it is logical to expect an elevation dependence. This dependence should be largely reduced when the atmospheric light becomes mainly diffuse, e.g., near sunset. Measurements by CLARKE and KELLY (1965), represented in Fig.54 suggest that this is the case.

To make the discussion of wavelength dependence more complete, BODEN's (1961) observations of twilight are presented in Fig.55.

TABLE XXIV

DOWNWARD IRRADIANCE ATTENUATION COEFFICIENT FOR DIFFERENT SOLAR ELEVA-
TIONS. OPTICAL DEPTH $\tau = 2.5$

(After Kozlyaninov and Pelevin, 1966)

Solar elevation (°)	Wavelength (nm)				
	430	480	550	600	650
15	0.081	0.060	0.063	0.089	0.20
29	0.072	0.055	0.059	0.082	0.17
59	0.058	0.045	0.049	0.068	0.14

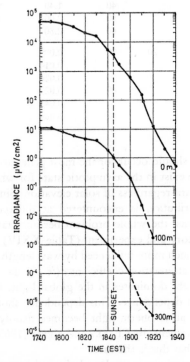

Fig.54. Downward irradiance (photomultiplier tube without colour filter) during sunset period in the western North Atlantic. (After Clarke and Kelly, 1965.)

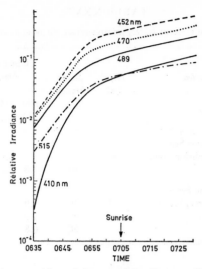

Fig.55. Spectral composition of downward irradiance at 100 m for the period of an hour around sunrise. (After BODEN, 1961.)

These show that the shortwave light becomes progressively more penetrating than the longwave light as time goes on. Boden mentions that the effect is possibly due to selective refraction at the sea surface; the present author is inclined to ascribe it to reflection changes according to the explanation given in Chapter 5, p.77.

Upward irradiance

It was first observed by SAUBERER and RUTTNER (1941) that the irradiance ratio E_u/E_d is dependent on the solar altitude, being

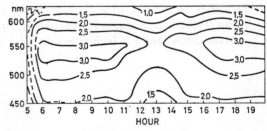

Fig.56. Diurnal change of the irradiance ratio E_u/E_d. (After AGERONOV, 1964.)

TABLE XXV

IRRADIANCE RATIO E_u/E_d AT DIFFERENT SOLAR ELEVATIONS

Region	Depth (m)	Solar elevation (°)	Wavelength (nm)		
			480 (%)	514 (%)	550 (%)
Sargasso Sea ("Dana" expedition, 1966)	50	30	5.5	3.1	
		60	3.8	2.2	
Baltic Sea (AHLQUIST, 1965)	20	10	1.9		1.1
		30	1.2		1.0
		50	0.8		0.9

higher for a low sun than for a high one. This effect, amply illustrated in Table XXV and Fig.56, is a consequence of the shape of the scattering function. Thus with a zenith sun in the water upward scattering from sun rays occurs at 90°–180°, and with a 45° sun at 45°–135°.

INFLUENCE OF BOTTOM

The upward irradiance E_u is normally affected by proximity to the bottom. In shallow waters, the accumulation of particles near the bottom may cause strong back-scattering. In Bermuda waters IVANOFF et al. (1961) found a logarithmic increase of the irradiance ratio E_u/E_d from 11 % at the surface to 29 % at 10 m, 1 m above the bottom. As shown by JOSEPH (1950), a minimum in E_u theoretically predicted develops at a certain depth above a high-reflecting sand bottom (Fig.30).

CHAPTER 11

POLARIZATION OF UNDERWATER RADIANT ENERGY

GENERAL POLARIZATION PATTERN

In order to form a true conception of the nature of polarization in the sea, we shall recollect that the light passing the sea surface is partly polarized (Chapter 4, p.68). Skylight shows a polarization structure within its refraction cone, and refracted sunlight is polarized in a degree which increases with its zenith angle. The polarization pattern of the penetrating light is radically altered when the light is scattered by water and particles. It is evident from radiance distributions that with increasing depth skylight becomes of decreasing importance compared with scattered light emanating chiefly from the direct sun rays. The general behaviour of the polarization of light scattered from a beam is outlined in Chapter 2. It is interesting to check these predictions against actual experimental findings. Such tests require that regard be paid to the dependence of polarization on the divergence of the incident beam (IVANOFF, 1957a; IVANOFF and LENOBLE, 1957).

OBSERVATIONS

In his first investigation, WATERMAN (1955) ascertained that polarization is dependent on the sun's position in the sky and persists down to 200 m depth; the polarization effect is ascribed to scattering of directional light. The effect of solar altitude has been carefully studied, mainly in horizontal lines of sight, by WATERMAN and WESTELL (1956). Their results agree with the theoretical prediction that maximum polarization occurs perpendicular to the sun beam. In a horizontal plane, the degree of polarization varies periodically with the azimuth to the solar bearing (Fig.57). The maximal points (peaks) at $\pm 90°$ are little affected by the solar altitude, whereas the

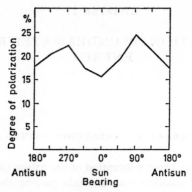

Fig. 57. Degree of polarization in horizontal lines of sight as a function of solar bearing. Solar elevation ~ 55°. (After WATERMAN and WESTELL, 1956.)

minimal points show a dependence on the altitude. The investigations of Waterman and Westell also demonstrate that all changes in parameters which diminish the directionality of underwater light, such as more diffuse atmospheric light, increased turbidity and the

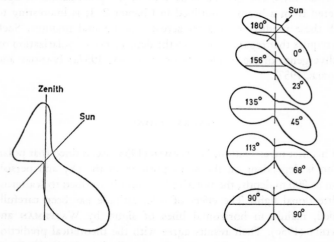

Fig.58. Degree of polarization (blue light) as a function of line of sight in the vertical plane of the sun. Off Corsica at 15 m depth. (After IVANOFF, 1957a.)

Fig.59. Angular distribution of degree of polarization in vertical planes of different azimuths from the sun. (After TIMOFEEVA, 1962.)

presence of bottom reflections tend to reduce the polarization. Observations by IVANOFF (1957a) for several lines of sight fit well in the theoretical pattern deduced by him on the basis of the radiance distribution. One of his diagrams (Fig.58) representing the degree of polarization in a vertical plane through the sun displays a marked dissimilarity between the two lobes of polarization at each side of the direction of the sun. This is partly ascribed to an effect of skylight polarization occurring between vertical angles of +45° and —45°. The systematic polarization experiments conducted by TIMOFEEVA (1962) have furnished a complete picture of the polarization distribution in vertical planes of different solar azimuths (to the solar bearing) (Fig.59). It is demonstrated that non-symmetry relative to the direction of the sun and the vertical appears for all azimuths except 90° due to the influence of the asymmetry of the sea's irradiance. Strict symmetry arises only for normal incidence of solar rays or with an overcast sky.

The correlation between degree of polarization and depth is consistent with the origin of polarization by scattering. The degree of

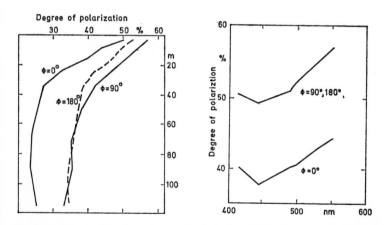

Fig.60. Influence of depth on degree of polarization (500 nm) in vertical planes of different azimuths in clear water. Solar elevation 22—30°. (After IVANOFF and WATERMAN, 1958b.)

Fig.61. Effect of wavelength on degree of polarization in vertical planes of 0° (solar bearing) and 90°, |180° in clear water. Solar elevation 57—61°. (After IVANOFF and WATERMAN, 1958b.)

polarization as a function of depth for vertical planes of different azimuths is exemplified in Fig.60 (IVANOFF and WATERMAN, 1958b). The p-value diminishes rapidly from 0 to 40 m due to a change of the radiance distribution from a markedly directed to a more diffuse character. The three curves depicted are likely to converge with increasing depth into one line of constant p when the asymptotic radiance distribution is approached. As directionality (from zenith) also prevails in the asymptotic state, there is every reason to believe that polarization of underwater light persists to infinite depths as predicted by the theory.

The dispersion of polarization is slight but definite. It accords with the general principle that the least directed, i.e., the least attenuated light (which is the blue in the ocean), displays the lowest degree of polarization (Fig.61) (IVANOFF, 1957b; IVANOFF and WATERMAN, 1958b; TIMOFEEVA, 1962).

CHAPTER 12

VISIBILITY

CONTRAST

Recognizing an object in water always involves the perception of differences in radiance or colour between the object and its surroundings. For visibility problems, therefore, we have to deal with the concepts of contrast and of contrast transmittance. If an object emits a radiance L, seen against a uniformly radiant background of radiance L_b, the contrast is defined by:

$$C = \frac{L-L_b}{L_b} \tag{62}$$

Thus the contrast varies from -1 for an ideal black object to ∞ for a radiant object observed against an ideal black background. In the latter case, since the object is detected only by direct rays which are not scattered, attenuation according to Allard's law reduces the radiance with progressively increased distance until it falls below the threshold of the eye.

In sea water a background always exists due to scattering, primary or multiple, of radiant energy emanating from the object. Prevailing daylight produces background scattering and in addition scattering through the path of sight to the eye, which results in a veil of light reducing the contrast.

THEORETICAL

Though notable contributions to the theory of underwater visibility have been made by SASAKI et al. (1952), IVANOFF (1957c), and SOKOLOV (1963), the achievements of the Visibility Laboratory have been predominant in this domain since DUNTLEY published his now classical work, *The Visibility of Submerged Objects* (1952). The essential features of the rigorous theory given by Duntley and his collaborators (DUNTLEY et al., 1957; DUNTLEY, 1963) are described below.

The treatment requires a further development of the concept of contrast pertaining to radiance (the colour contrast problem is not considered). If the object and the background have radiances L_o and L_{bo} when observed at zero distance, and L_r and L_{br} when observed at distance r, then we may introduce inherent contrast C_o and apparent contrast C_r by the definitions:

$$C_o = \frac{L_o - L_{bo}}{L_{bo}} \tag{63}$$

$$C_r = \frac{L_r - L_{br}}{L_{br}} \tag{64}$$

We shall now consider an object or target at depth z_t and at distance r from an observer at depth z; the path of sight has zenith angle θ and azimuth ϕ, and $z_t - z = r \cos \theta$.

The attenuation of the radiance of daylight, or the field radiance in a uniform medium, is given by:

$$\frac{dL(z, \theta, \phi)}{dr} = -K(z, \theta, \phi) \cos \theta\, L(z, \theta, \phi)$$

We recall that the attenuation coefficient K is constant for certain paths of sight and that it becomes constant for all directions in the asymptotic radiance distribution.

The transfer of field radiance is given by eq.45:

$$\frac{dL(z, \theta, \phi)}{dr} = -cL(z, \theta, \phi) + L_*(z, \theta, \phi)$$

and analogously for the apparent target radiance L_t:

$$\frac{dL_t(z, \theta, \phi)}{dr} = -cL_t(z, \theta, \phi) + L_*(z, \theta, \phi)$$

A combination of the last three equations, and integration over the entire path of sight, results in the following expression:

$$L_{tr}(z, \theta, \phi) = L_{to}(z_t, \theta, \phi)e^{-cr} + L(z_t, \theta, \phi)e^{K(z, \theta, \phi)r \cos \theta} \times$$
$$\times (1 - e^{-cr + K(z, \theta, \phi)r \cos \theta}) \tag{65}$$

This completely describes the relation between the inherent radiance L_{to} and the apparent target radiance L_{tr}. The first term on the right accounts for the attenuation of image-forming light from the target, and the second indicates gain by scattering of ambient light throughout the path of sight. Attention must be paid to the possible variation of $K(z, \theta, \phi)$ over the path of sight.

By replacing the subscript t by b in eq.65, an analogous form representing the background is obtained. By subtracting the apparent background radiance from the apparent target radiance, the important relation:

$$L_{tr}(z, \theta, \phi) - L_{br}(z, \theta, \phi) = \left[L_{to}(z_t, \theta, \phi) - L_{bo}(z_t, \theta, \phi) \right] e^{-cr} \quad (66)$$

is found. This proves that the radiance differences between target and background follow the attenuation law of a beam, since the factor $e^{-cr} = T_r$ is the beam transmittance along the path of sight. By introducing the definition of contrast according to eq. 63 and 64, the ratio of apparent contrast to inherent contrast may be written:

$$\frac{C_r(z, \theta, \phi)}{C_o(z_t, \theta, \phi)} = T_r(z, \theta, \phi) \frac{L_{bo}(z_t, \theta, \phi)}{L_{br}(z, \theta, \phi)} \quad (67)$$

This equation represents the general case, and holds true for non-uniform water and for different levels of ambient daylight.

Another expression for the significant contrast ratio is obtained by combining eq.65 and 66 with the definition of contrast so as to eliminate the apparent target and background radiances:

$$\frac{C_o(z_t, \theta, \phi)}{C_r(z, \theta, \phi)} = 1 - \frac{L(z_t, \theta, \phi)}{L_{bo}(z_t, \theta, \phi)} \left(1 - e^{cr - K(z, \theta, \phi) r \cos \theta} \right) \quad (68)$$

Some special cases are of interest. With an object in deep water, the inherent background radiance may be considered as identical with the field radiance, i.e., $L(z_t, \theta, \phi) = L_{bo}(z_t, \theta, \phi)$. This yields the simple form:

$$\frac{C_r(z, \theta, \phi)}{C_o(z_t, \theta, \phi)} = e^{-cr + K(z, \theta, \phi) r \cos \theta} \quad (69)$$

For horizontal paths of sight we have $\cos \theta = 0$, and the equation reduces to:

$$\frac{C_r(z, \pi/2, \phi)}{C_o(z_t, \pi/2, \phi)} = e^{-cr} \quad (70)$$

This single formula is a fully adequate expression for the reduction of contrast for all kinds of targets.

MEASUREMENTS

Research on underwater visibility has been profitably stimulated by developments in atmospheric vision. Sighting ranges in sea water are determined by the attenuation coefficient, and even in the clearest water they are diminutive compared to those in the atmosphere. In consequence, predictions of sighting ranges are needed for the important practical applications of underwater visibility, e.g., underwater diving. Nomographic charts have been prepared at the Visibility Laboratory on the basis of the above theory for objects of arbitrary size — also Secchi disks — as a function of attenuation coefficient, depth, solar elevation, target reflectance, bottom reflectance, etc. The charts have been checked against field experiments, and their validity proved. Simple rules of thumb are useful in practical work. DUNTLEY (1963) mentions that the underwater sighting range for most objects is 4 to 5 times the distance:

$$1/(c - K(z) \cos \theta)$$

and that along horizontal paths of sight large dark objects seen as silhouettes against a water background can be sighted at the distance $4/c$.

Little evidence is as yet available for deep water. An important contribution has been made by COUSTEAU et al. (1964) who, at different dephts off Corsica, measured the radiance at maximal distances of 360 m from a submerged lamp in horizontal directions. It was found that a lamp of 500 W is visible to the human eye at distances as great as 275 m.

VISIBILITY OF FIELD RADIANCE

LE GRAND (1954) has made computations which suggest that the dark-adapted human eye can perceive light down to at least 800 m in the clear ocean. Actual observations from the bathyscaphe indicate that the limit of visibility lies between 600 and 700 m. No systematic investigation has been made in different water types regarding the depth levels at which field radiance falls below the threshold of the eye.

CHAPTER 13

COLOUR OF THE SEA

DEFINITIONS

The discussion of the colour problem brings a special aspect to marine optics. We have now to deal exclusively with light, i.e., the radiant energy which is capable of stimulating the human eye. The visible spectrum is regarded as covering the small band between 380 and 770 nm, but its limits are ill defined.

Definitions of the fundamental colorimetric concepts are not included in Chapter 1, which gives an account of the radiometric terms only; for detailed information about colorimetry the reader is referred to the publication by the Commission Internationale de l'Éclairage (ANONYMOUS, 1957). In the context of colour it is proper to speak about luminance and illuminance instead of radiance and irradiance.

PERCEPTION OF COLOUR

Colour is not a question of the physics of light only, but is also a sensation. In the perception of colour the retina image is the immediate stimulus which creates a response process involving a chain of physiological events. The last stage is the mental interpretation, which is complex and affected by experience and associations of different kinds. A characteristic feature is that colour is considered as belonging to the object in view or caused by the illuminant. In regard to its psychological aspect, it is no wonder that the colour problem has been the subject of a great number of theories (BORN, 1963). Attention is drawn to some significant facts about colour vision. Colour perception is most highly developed in the central part of the retina, which contains only cones. The rods are used mainly for low intensity vision, which is in monochrome. It has been known for a long time, already formulated in the Young–Helmholtz' theory, that the normal human eye is trichromatic. Recent colour research has detected the presence of three independent receptors as discrete units in the cone's outer limbs, and their spectral response is becoming known. In essence, trichromaticity implies that any colour can be matched with a mixture of three independent colours provided that no one of these can be matched by mixing the other two.

COLORIMETRIC SYSTEM

A colour specification aims at expressing colour as synonymous with a dominant wavelength of light on the basis of a system which considers any colour as synthesized by a mixture of three components which may be described as red, green and blue. The C.I.E. (1933) standard colorimetric system for evaluating any spectral distribution of energy is generally employed. The sequence of basic definitions is briefly outlined here.

The numerical description of colour is based on the tristimulus values of the spectrum colours, or the colour mixture data which are given the symbols $\bar{x}_\lambda$, $\bar{y}_\lambda$ and $\bar{z}_\lambda$. These are hypothetical standard values chosen so that $\bar{y}_\lambda$ is identical with the standard luminosity curve for photopic vision by the normal eye (see also COMMITTEE ON COLORIMETRY, 1963). The standard functions are shown in Table XXVI for an equal energy spectrum.

For any coloured light source the spectral properties of which are given by E_λ, the tristimulus values X, Y and Z are determined by the following integrals:

$$X = \int E_\lambda \bar{x}_\lambda \, d\lambda$$

$$Y = \int E_\lambda \bar{y}_\lambda \, d\lambda$$

$$Z = \int E_\lambda \bar{z}_\lambda \, d\lambda$$

These components can be added, and the ratio of each component to the sum of the three form the chromaticity coordinates x, y and z:

$$x = \frac{X}{X+Y+Z} \qquad y = \frac{Y}{X+Y+Z} \qquad z = \frac{Z}{X+Y+Z}$$

Since $x+y+z = 1$, two coordinates suffice to represent the colour in a chromaticity diagram. Usually x and y are plotted in a rectangular diagram.

For a constant value of E_λ, the chromaticity coordinates $x = y = z = 0.333$ define the white point or the achromatic colour S in the diagram. The numerical value of colour is geometrically derived by drawing a line from the white point S through the plotted colour Q. (Fig.63). The intersection A of this line with the locus curve of the spectrum specifies the dominant wavelength. The other significant factor, purity, is equivalent to the ratio QS/AS.

TABLE XXVI

THE C. I. E. COLOUR MIXTURE DATA FOR EQUAL ENERGY SPECTRUM

Wave-length (nm)	$\bar{x}_\lambda$	$\bar{y}_\lambda$	$\bar{z}_\lambda$	Wave-length (nm)	$\bar{x}_\lambda$	$\bar{y}_\lambda$	$\bar{z}_\lambda$
380	0.0023	0.0000	0.0106	580	1.8320	1.7396	0.0032
390	0.0082	0.0002	0.0391	590	2.0535	1.5144	0.0023
400	0.0283	0.0007	0.1343	600	2.1255	1.2619	0.0016
410	0.0840	0.0023	0.4005	610	2.0064	1.0066	0.0007
420	0.2740	0.0082	1.3164	620	1.7065	0.7610	0.0003
430	0.5667	0.0232	2.7663	630	1.2876	0.5311	0.0000
440	0.6965	0.0458	3.4939	640	0.8945	0.3495	
450	0.6730	0.0761	3.5470	650	0.5681	0.2143	
460	0.5824	0.1197	3.3426	660	0.3292	0.1218	
470	0.3935	0.1824	2.5895	670	0.1755	0.0643	
480	0.1897	0.2772	1.6193	680	0.0927	0.0337	
490	0.0642	0.4162	0.9313	690	0.0457	0.0165	
500	0.0097	0.6473	0.5455	700	0.0225	0.0081	
510	0.0187	1.0077	0.3160	710	0.0117	0.0042	
520	0.1264	1.4172	0.1569	720	0.0057	0.0020	
530	0.3304	1.7243	0.0841	730	0.0028	0.0010	
540	0.5810	1.9077	0.0408	740	0.0014	0.0006	
550	0.8670	1.9906	0.0174	750	0.0006	0.0002	
560	1.1887	1.9896	0.0077	760	0.0003	0.0001	
570	1.5243	1.9041	0.0042	770	0.0001	0.0000	
Totals					21.3713	21.3714	21.3715

THEORIES OF THE COLOUR OF THE SEA

Many theories have been advanced to explain the blue colour of clear ocean water and the change of colour caused by increasing turbidity. It is nowadays generally accepted that the blue colour owes its origin to selective absorption by the water itself, which acts as a monochromator for blue light. The old absorption theory of BUNSEN (1847) thus affords the principal explanation as far as it concerns the blue colour of clear water. The SORET theory (1869), which attributes the blue colour entirely to scattering, contains a part of the truth. As emphasized by RAMAN (1922), molecular scattering plays a significant role. It is borne out by radiance and irradiance measurements (Chapter 10) that the clearest waters display a backscatter which emanates to a great extent from multiple molecular scattering, and therefore shifts the colour toward shorter wavelengths. KALLE (1938, 1939b) has critically examined existing theories. He has emphatically proved the role of molecular scattering in clear water and presented the new idea that yellow substance is largely responsible for the change of colour towards longer wavelengths in turbid waters. LENOBLE (1956d) has made colour computations applying Chandrasekhar's method with the assumption of nonselective scattering. For clear water illuminated by a uniformly white sky, it was proved that the colour is close to the transmittance peak of water and thus essentially an absorption effect.

COLOUR OBSERVED ABOVE THE SEA

The colour of the sea viewed from a point above the surface is spectacularly beautiful. Several factors conspire to make the sea a scene of incessant colour changes: white glitter from the sun, reflected blue skylight, dark shadows of clouds and the blue or green light scattered back from subsurface levels. In clear weather the last component produced by sunlight lends a distinct colour to the sea, whereas with diffuse conditions the light nonselectively reflected dominates and the sea looks colourless and grey (KALLE, 1939b). Rippling and ruffling of the surface greatly enhances the colour because of reduced reflection (RAMAN, 1922). Likewise, waves seen from the lee side are more intensely coloured than from the windward side (SHOULEIKIN, 1923). HULBURT (1934) has pointed out that for a breezy sea the blue in the reflected skylight which emanates from the sky at 30° (Chapter 5) is usually bluer than that which comes from near the horizon. Hence a colour contrast arises between the sea and the horizon.

COLOUR OBSERVED IN SITU

The oceanographic concept of colour refers more adequately to colour in situ, which does not involve light reflected from the water surface. In situ colour may be studied by direct visual observations employing colour measuring tubes the lower ends of which are submerged below the surface (KALLE, 1938; KOZLYANINOV, 1961).

The initial investigations by Kalle apply the tristimulus system of Haschek and Haitinger, which employs colour mixture data different from those of C.I.E. The triangular representation in Fig.62 exhibits colour values from various areas and reveals several fundamental features. The colour of such relatively turbid waters as the North

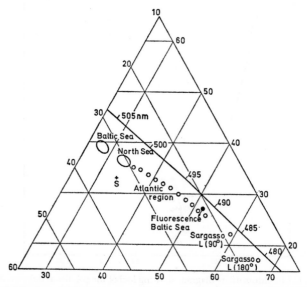

Fig.62. Haschek—Haitinger chromaticity triangle showing loci of colours for various regions of the sea. (After KALLE, 1939b.)

Sea and the Baltic is a mixture of colours of various components, and its purity is therefore low. The colour from below in the Sargasso Sea is more shortwave and more saturated than is the colour in the horizontal direction because selective scattering is more active in the upwelling light. Chromaticity coordinates for the fluorescence of Baltic water are also inserted in the diagram which determines the fluorescent colour at 488 nm. However, the contribution of fluorescence to colour of the sea has so far been little studied.

Wholly objective colour information is furnished by spectral distribution of irradiance and radiance subjected to a colour analysis in terms of the C.I.E. chromaticity coordinates. As an example, a chromaticity chart for the Sargasso Sea data in Fig.63 exhibits the typical features of clear water. In this case we have in view the colour of a horizontal surface facing upwards for downward irradiance and downwards for upward irradiance. The figures marked at the colour loci indicate the depths in meters.

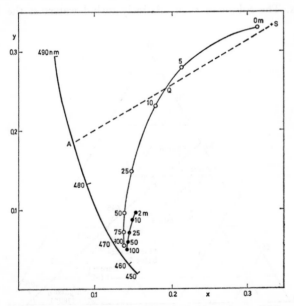

Fig.63. C.I.E. chromaticity diagram showing loci of the colours at different depths of downward illuminance (longer curve) and of upward illuminance (shorter curve) in the Sargasso Sea.

This diagram offers a perspective on colour as a function of depth. The curvature of the locus of the downward component is indicative of the selective absorption process effected by the water. The colour at the surface is 491 nm. Such a greenish-blue hue can be observed in shallow waters with a reflecting bottom (DUNTLEY, 1963), or against a blue background in propeller-disturbed water where air bubbles reflect light to the observer. It is noted in Fig.63 that at small depths, even at 10 m, blue light (482 nm) falls on the horizontal surface and the blue colour becomes gradually saturated down to the last measured point of 100 m (466 nm). The locus of the upward component, on the other hand, is a short and nearly straight line representing a colour change from 470 nm at the surface to 464 nm at 100 m. As we have seen, this colour is to some degree the result of selective multiple scattering by the water.

The two loci for downward and upward illuminance are close, and seem to converge towards a colour of 462 nm with 100 % purity. In other words, the final outcome of the colour selective process at

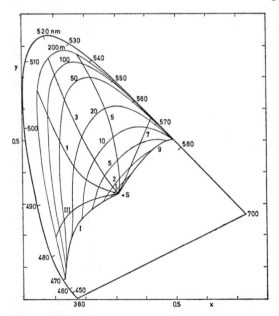

Fig.64. C.I.E. chromaticity diagram showing loci of the colours of downward illuminance at different depths in optical water types.

TABLE XXVII

COLOUR EVALUATED FROM SPECTRAL ENERGY DISTRIBUTION OF UPWARD IRRADIANCE

Station	Position		Solar elevation (°)	Depth (m)	Colour (mμ)	Purity (%)
Pacific Ocean	S	01° 20′	61	2	473	85
142	E	167° 23′		5	473	87
				10	473	89
				25	472	92
				50	469	95
Indian Ocean	S	11° 25′	31	10	472	90
191	E	102° 13′		50	469	97
192	S	11° 25′	80	2	474	84
	E	102° 08′		10	473	87
				25	472	92
				50	469	94
Mediterranean	N	33° 54′	74	0	473	83
277	E	28° 17′		5	473	86
				10	473	87
				25	472	92
				50	470	95
Atlantic Ocean	N	32°	70	0	483	71
off Bermuda	W	65°				
Sargasso Sea	N	26° 50′	62	2	470	86
	W	63° 30′		10	470	88
				25	468	92
				50	467	95
				100	465	97
			25	1	471	85
				10	470	88
				25	469	91
				50	468	93
				100	466	95
Baltic Sea	N	60°	55	0	540	24
	E	19°		10	551	73
				20	553	87

300–400 m is blue light of 462 nm from all directions around the observation point. The wavelength of the residual light at these levels is obviously equivalent to the wavelength of maximum trans-mittance. Attention is called to the fact that an isotropic colour distribution prevails at levels where the approach to an asymptotic radiance distribution is not yet complete.

The chromaticity diagram in Fig.64 exhibits loci of downward illuminance for the existing water types. It is noted that the oceanic colour is close to 470 nm, whereas the colour of coastal waters of types *1–9* is conspicuously changed towards longer wavelengths on account of the selective action of particles and yellow substance.

Since a special interest attaches to the colour of upwardly scattered light, colour data evaluated from upward irradiance at different depths are assembled in Table XXVII. The numerical value of colour at the surface extends from 462 nm in the clearest waters to 540 nm in the most turbid (Baltic Sea). Decreasing solar elevation tends to change colour and purity in the same way as does increasing depth (Chapter 10).

In situ colour varies with the direction of observation. An analysis of spectral radiance rather than irradiance, gives some insight into colour as a function of vertical and azimuthal angle. Table XXVIII summarizes some data obtained from spectral radiances. It is evident that the angular distribution of colour has not yet been scanned in

TABLE XXVIII

COLOUR EVALUATED FROM SPECTRAL ENERGY DISTRIBUTION OF RADIANCE IN SURFACE WATER

Region	Solar elevation (°)	Vertical angle of radiance (°)	Colour (nm)	Purity (%)	Reference
Sargasso Sea	60	180 (nadir)	475	85	"Dana" expedition, 1966
		+ 90	482	80	
North Sea		180	502	37	KALLE (1939b)
Baltic Sea		180	512	32	
Gulf Stream		180	478	84	DUNTLEY (1963)
Californian coast	27	+ 90	519	8	TYLER (1964)

detail. It may be anticipated that a fine structure occurs in the refraction cone $2 \cdot 48.6°$, which includes white sunlight as well as blue skylight.

ABSORPTION BY PARTICLES AND YELLOW SUBSTANCE

The influence on colour of particles and coloured dissolved matter, chiefly yellow substance merits particular attention. Overall decreased transmittance is accompanied by a shift of peak transmittance toward longer wavelengths, which appears as a colour change from blue via green to brown. There is evidence that this is a consequence of increased selective absorption by particles and yellow substance. KALLE (1938) and JOSEPH (1955) have thoroughly investigated the significant role of yellow substance as an absorbing medium for shortwave light. ATKINS and POOLE (1958) believe that the reversal and variations in the green/blue attenuation coefficient ratio is partly due to absorption by chlorophyll, carotenoids and xantophylls in the phytoplankton. Contributions by YENTSCH and RYTHER (1959) and YENTSCH (1960) stress the importance of absorption in the blue by photosynthetic pigments of phytoplankton. TYLER (1964) men-

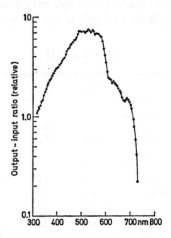

Fig.65. The radiance (output) in a horizontal direction is compared to the total irradiance (input) falling on the surface. Note absorption band at 680 nm due to chlorophyll. (After TYLER and SMITH, 1966.)

tions that chlorophyll is a major factor in the colour observed in the horizontal direction off the coast of California as the absorption spectrum of chlorophyll appears in his radiance curves (Fig.65). As will be remembered, coloured particles cause wavelength selectivity in absorption (Table IX) and, to some extent, in scattering (Chapter 2).

DISCOLORATION OF THE SEA

Discoloration of the sea visible to an observer above the surface is commonly caused by exceptionally dense populations of marine phytoplankton, sometimes by swarming zooplankton and, very rarely, by air-borne sand or volcanic dust. The well known phenomena of red tides and marine water blooms are generally due to various species of phytoplankton.

It follows from what has been stated about upwelling light in the sea that the amount of back-scattered light is proportional to the total cross section of the particles. The size of the dominant organism is therefore important. HART (1966) mentions that 20 cells/ml of *Noctiluca*, 570 filaments/ml of *Trichodesmium*, and 6,000 cells/ml of the small thecate dinoflagellate *Peridinium triquetrum* are each capable of producing visible discoloration. For further details the reader is referred to Hart's complete description of the phenomenon of discoloured water.

PART III

Applications of Optical Methods

CHAPTER 14

APPLICATIONS TO PHYSICAL OCEANOGRAPHY

OBJECT OF OPTICAL APPLICATIONS

The optical properties of sea water and the propagation and distribution of underwater light are dependent on the physical, chemical and dynamic conditions of the sea. As a consequence, optical data may be utilized in various ways to gain information about oceanographic conditions, in particular dynamic conditions. Rewarding efforts at implementation have been made, and optical applications in oceanographic research are rapidly gaining ground. It has become clear that scattering and beam transmittance measurements supply substantial knowledge about two constituents in the sea, viz. particles and yellow substance. The oceanographic interest in the distribution of these components is dictated by the desire to find suitable parameters for characterizing water masses. The primary advantage of optical methods is the relative ease by which data can be obtained even in rough weather.

The supreme importance of underwater light for marine biological studies merits treatment in a special Chapter (15). It is also clear that the absorption of the radiant energy by the sea is a fundamental factor in the thermodynamics of the sea. As already mentioned, however, we must refrain from dealing with thermodynamical transfer processes and related problems of heat economy, since this subject is too large to be embraced by the present account.

REFLECTION AND REFRACTION

The reflection and refraction of sunlight at the sea surface are indicative of the state of the surface. This is brought out in the aforementioned glitter theories (Chapter 5, p.75). The deductions of the slopes of the sea surface made by Cox and MUNK (1956) show that the observed, nearly Gaussian distribution of slopes is consistent with a continuous wave spectrum of arbitrary width or with a large number of discrete frequencies.

The refracted glitter is also dependent on wave action. SCHENCK (1957) has studied the phenomenon of bright bands of light moving across a shallow sea bottom at the same velocity as the waves. The intensification of radiance is ascribed to lens action by the waves. In this context, it may be mentioned that the heights of water waves produced in a laboratory tank can be observed by fluctuations in the absorption of light passing vertically through the water (FALLER, 1958).

DISTRIBUTION OF PARTICLES

Scattering measurements

There is adequate ground for treating separately the oceanographic application of scattering observations, since they provide the most sensitive means of exploring the particle distribution as was first demonstrated by KALLE (1939a). Some conspicuous results indicate that the particle content may be considered to be an inherent property of the water mass. An example of clear identification is given in Fig.66. The Pacific water present below 1,000 m depth has passed several sills before reaching the deep Flores Basin. In spite of the long duration of this transport, it has apparently maintained its

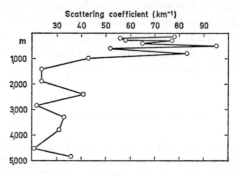

Fig.66. Particle stratification in the Flores Basin, showing the inflow of clear Pacific water between 800 and 1,400 m. (After JERLOV, 1959.)

integrity and remained unaffected by the turbid water in the surface layers. At present, definite conclusions can be drawn neither about the refractory character of particulate matter which is transported over long distances nor about the rate of continual supply of particles from above to a spreading water mass.

An important aspect of the particle problem is the formation of optical scattering layers frequently encountered at various levels in the sea. RILEY et al. (1949) have considered theoretically the distribution of phytoplankton in an uppermost layer of the ocean with a constant eddy diffusion, and found that a maximum is developed near the lower limit of the photic zone. WYRTKI (1950) has discussed the significant role of the vertical gradient of the eddy diffusion in forming the particle distribution pattern. Below the photic zone, the mechanism at which a maximum is developed requires not only that the eddy diffusion increases with depth but also that the sinking rate of the particles be reduced, i.e., their buoyancy be improved (JERLOV, 1959). The necessary conditions are generally fulfilled for a discontinuity layer which shows high vertical stability. NEUYMIN and SOROKINA (1964) and PARAMONOV (1965) have thoroughly investigated the relation between stability and distribution of particles. They found that in the upper layers down to 150 m the predicted distribution does not invariably correlate with stability, on account of migrations of living organisms. Vertical movements of water occurring at upwellings or at divergences and convergences are generally indicated by the particle content, as they lead to salient changes of the productivity of the sea (see Fig.82).

The spreading of water masses in the deep sea is often reflected in particle diagrams. A conspicuous situation in Fig.67 demonstrates that the tongue of high-salinity water from the subtropical convergence in the Pacific is fairly rich in particles. The intruding water mass as a rule has higher particle content than the surrounding water. It is difficult to judge to what extent this is an inherent property of the water mass originating from surface levels or an effect of the turbulence created by the flow of the water masses. The occurrence of strata of such high particle concentration as that extending at the 6° level in Fig.67 is in many cases associated with a defined water mass. In other instances one fails to find any relationship. The initial scattering data obtained by KALLE (1939a) in deep Atlantic water indicate that particle maxima are strong and numerous (Fig.68).

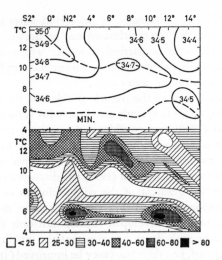

Fig.67. Stratum with high-particle concentration in the salinity minimum. Tongue of high-salinity water from the subtropical convergence rich in particles. Meridional section near longitude 150° W in the Pacific. (After JERLOV, 1959.)

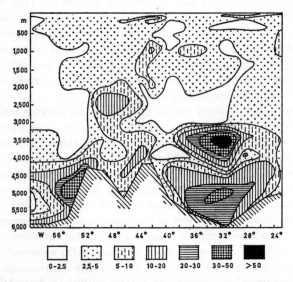

Fig.68. Particle maxima in a west–east vertical section near the Tropic of Cancer in the Atlantic. (After KALLE, 1939a.)

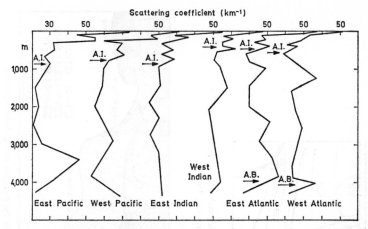

Fig.69. Depth profiles of scattering in the oceans, indicating spreading of Antarctic Intermediate (A.I.) and Antarctic Bottom water (A.B.). (After JERLOV, 1959.)

This circumstance is supported by JERLOV's (1953a) measurements in the equatorial region. Several problems in marine chemistry and geology must be treated with due regard to the particle component. In that connection, some guidance about average or typical vertical distributions as derived from scattering observations is obtainable from Fig.69. The profiles which represent exclusively the equatorial regions indicate that at great depths the western Atlantic has the highest relative particle concentration, whereas minimal amounts are encountered in the western Pacific.

The spreading in the sea of turbid river water or other freshwater discharge is readily studied by scattering measurements. KETCHUM and SHONTING (1958) have traced the flow of the turbid Orinoco water in the Cariaco Trench. Another example of particle distribution from off the Po River proves the existence of a deep countercurrent which flows against the turbid surface water (JERLOV, 1958).

Beam transmittance measurements

The beam transmittance meter has developed into a powerful tool for identifying water masses, as evidenced by a great number of investigations (JOSEPH, 1955, 1959, 1961; NISHIZAWA et al., 1959; WYRTKI, 1960; PAVLOV, 1961; SCHEMAINDA, 1962; DERA, 1963;

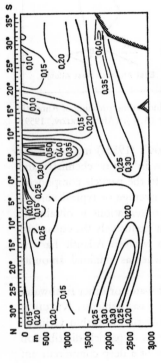

Fig.70. Distribution of beam transmittance in a meridional section near longitude 171° W in the Pacific. (After KOZLYANNOV, 1960.)

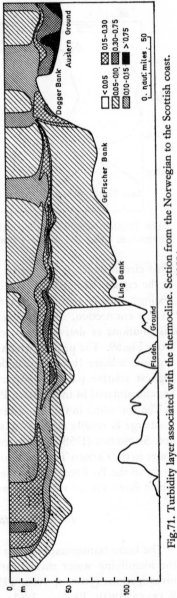

Fig.71. Turbidity layer associated with the thermocline. Section from the Norwegian to the Scottish coast. (After JOSEPH, 1955.)

NEUYMIN et al., 1964; BALL and LAFOND, 1964; and MALMBERG, 1964). Beam transmittance, if recorded in the red, is a measure of the particle content, though it is a less sensitive parameter than scatterance. Its relation to dynamics is analogous to that of scatterance.

A section of vertical particle distribution in Fig.70 serves to illustrate the usefulness of beam transmittance as an oceanographic parameter. Note that the prominent features of the section in Fig.67 are only vaguely indicated in Fig.70, which is situated farther to the west. Instead, attention is drawn to the huge stratum of turbid water present at 2,000–2,500 m. It is interesting to note that the profiles in Fig.69 display similar maxima. Both JERLOV (1959) and KOZLYANINOV (1960) think that they result from the flow of Antarctic water. Furthermore, a large-scale comparison between dynamic sections and distributions of beam transmittance made by KOZLYANINOV and OVCHINNIKOV (1961) shows correlations between the structure of the current pattern and the broad outlines of the beam transmittances.

Convincing proof of the capability of the beam transmittance meter to detect the discontinuity layer and record its movements is furnished first and foremost by JOSEPH (1955). A section between the Scottish and the Norwegian coast (Fig.71) shows that the thermocline is associated with a layer rich in particles. This is not split up until over the deep Norwegian trench where the Baltic current influences the structure of the surface water. On the basis of beam transmittance measurements, JOSEPH and SENDNER (1958) have elaborated a new approach to the problem of horizontal diffusion in the sea and have induced a fruitful development in this domain. VOITOV (1964) has utilized the transmittance method to measure vertical eddy diffusion as a function of depth.

Particle distribution near the bottom

The turbulence effected by bottom currents generally leads to an increase of particle content towards the bottom. Only if currents vanish, or if the bottom is uncovered, is the bottom layer uniform in particles. The existing turbulence is obviously much influenced by topographic features. In a systematic study of oceanic particle distribution, JERLOV (1953a) has shown that clouds of particles are frequently encountered at levels 10–50 m above the bottom. This is

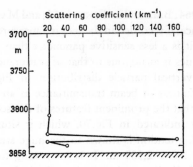

Fig.72. Example of particle cloud above the bottom.   (After JERLOV, 1953a.)

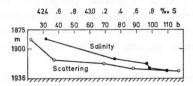

Fig.73. Particle accumulation in the high-salinity water near the bottom of the Red Sea. (After JERLOV, 1953a.)

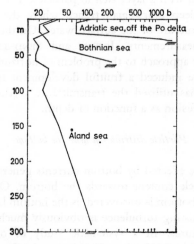

Fig.74. Logarithmic increase of particle content toward bottom in the Baltic and in the Adriatic Sea. (After JERLOV, 1955a, 1958.)

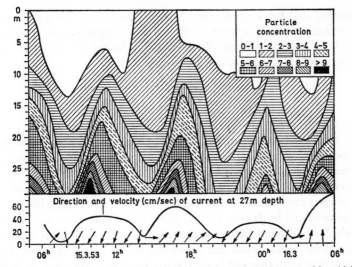

Fig.75. Periodic rising and sinking of sediment in the North Sea caused by tidal currents. (After JOSEPH, 1955.)

interpreted as an effect of lateral transport from adjacent topographic heights (Fig.72). It is a matter of particular interest that the high-salinity water found at the greatest depths in the Red Sea is rich in particles (Fig.73).

In shallow waters a logarithmic increase towards the bottom is evidenced in some cases (Fig.74). The distribution in the Bothnian Gulf indicates slow settling of organic material under the influence of horizontal flow (JERLOV, 1955a; FUKUDA, 1960). Similar distributions in the North Sea (Fig.75; JOSEPH, 1955) and in the Adriatic Sea (Fig.74; JERLOV, 1958) are attributed to periodic rising and sinking of sediment for which the tidal currents are the chief agency. Other observations do not suggest any systematic change of the particle content, e.g., IVANOFF's (1960b) data from 50 to 600 m depth off Monaco. PICKARD and GIOVANDO (1960) have pointed out the role of turbidity currents as the cause of particle abundance near the bottom.

Pollution research

Extensive applications of scatterance and beam transmittance meters are found in pollution research. The method rests on the finding that for a given type of particulate matter the attenuation coefficient is proportional to the particle concentration expressed as mass per unit volume (WYRTKI, 1953; JOSEPH, 1955; JONES and WILLS, 1956; OCHAKOVSKY, 1966a).

DISTRIBUTION OF YELLOW SUBSTANCE

Yellow substance may be treated as a semi-conservative concentration which is readily determined by means of beam transmittance measurements. The analysis presumes its presence in fairly high concentrations such as are generally encountered in coastal waters. Original experiments in the Baltic conducted by KALLE (1949) and corroborated by JERLOV (1955a) prove that diagrams of the content of yellow substance plotted against salinity yield excellent information about the water masses and the mixing between them (Fig.76). The very first scattering and beam transmittance measurements made by PETTERSSON (1936) showed that the Baltic water flowing northwards along the west coast of Sweden is clearly identified by its colour due to yellow substance. It is evident from Fig.77 which represents these

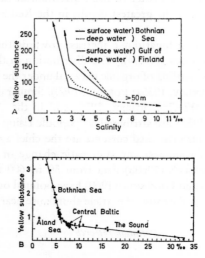

Fig.76. Relationship between salinity and amount of yellow substance in the Baltic. A. After KALLE (1949). B. After JERLOV (1955a).

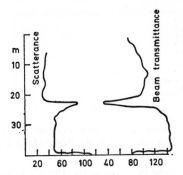

Fig.77. Comparison of scatterance and beam transmittance (in the blue) for water off the Swedish west coast indicating stronger absorption in the top layer of partly Baltic water than in the underlying Skagerrak water. (After PETTERSSON, 1936.)

results, that the upper layer of water of partly Baltic origin absorbs more strongly in the blue than does the underlying Skagerrak water of higher salinity; an accumulation of particles occurs at the boundary between the two water masses.

DISTRIBUTION OF FLUORESCENCE

The use of fluorescent dyes as tracers in order to study diffusion in the sea is another beautiful example of an optical method applied to a significant dynamical problem. Rhodamine B is generally selected as a suitable dye on account of its relatively low cost, high detectability and relatively good stability.

The method aims at exciting rhodamine B, preferably by the green mercury line which can be isolated, e.g., by an interference filter. The exciting light is filtered from the emitted path by an orange Schott filter OG 2, so that light scattered by particles is eliminated. Tests are usually made by means of a laboratory meter on collected water samples or on water brought up under positive pressure with the aid of a pumping system. More adequate in situ measurement is hampered by the superposed effect of ambient natural light. This difficulty is overcome for a meter which is provided with two measuring units; both of them face downwards but with only one receiv-

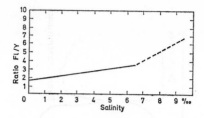

Fig.78. Relationship between salinity and ratio of amount of fluorescent matter to amount of yellow substance in the Baltic. (After KALLE, 1949.)

ing the fluorescent light (KULLENBERG, 1967a). It may also be expedient to use a chopped light source in the fluorimeter.

It follows from Chapter 3 that natural fluorescence is a characteristic property of the same utility as yellow substance. KALLE (1949) has proved that in coastal waters the ratio of fluorescent substance to yellow substance is a suitable parameter to be plotted against salinity (Fig.78).

CHAPTER 15

APPLICATIONS TO MARINE BIOLOGY

PRIMARY PRODUCTION

Light penetration

The physics of radiant energy is of direct importance for evaluating the result of the photosynthetic activity in the sea. The penetration of light defines the photic zone, the lower limit of which is generally marked by the depth where surface irradiance is reduced to 1%. This significant level is depicted in Fig.79 as a function of the wavelength for the different types of ocean water classified in Chapter 10 (p.120). It is clear that the zone is shallow in the red, and that overall increased turbidity reduces the shortwave part of the spectrum more strongly than the longwave part. This diagram, in conjunction with the regional chart of distribution of optical water types (Fig.50), yields general information about the depth of the photic zone in some oceanic areas. With a dense station net, it is possible to represent the topography of the 1% level. Such a pattern off the Strait of

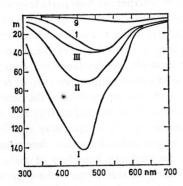

Fig.79. Depths at which downward irradiance is 1% of the surface value in the different water types.

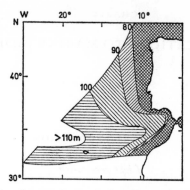

Fig.80. Topography of the level of 1 % of surface downward irradiance off the Strait of Gibraltar. (After JERLOV and NYGÅRD, 1961.)

Gibraltar (Fig.80) illustrates the presence of turbid water along the coasts, and the extension of clear water from west-northwest close to the Strait consistent with the general flow. Another significant parameter is the attenuation of energy in the interval 350–700 nm, which is found to be active in photosynthesis. Relevant information for the different water types is given in terms of percentage of surface irradiance by the family of curves in Fig.81.

Distribution of particles and yellow substance

The question arises whether the total particle content as determined by scattering measurements could be indicative of the distribution of oceanic productivity. There is ample evidence that the horizontal particle pattern is largely effected by dynamical processes, especially upwelling. As an example, results from the equatorial Pacific are adduced which exhibit a close congruence even in details between the particle distribution and the topography of the depth of the thermocline or the topography of the sea surface (Fig.82). An abundance of particles occurs in the upwelling area near the Galapagos, which merges into the sharply defined equator divergence region. Even the divergence at the northern boundary of the countercurrent at 10° N shows up clearly in this picture. Another upwelling in the divergence between the south equatorial current and the countercurrent in the Indian Ocean is also clearly established by the high

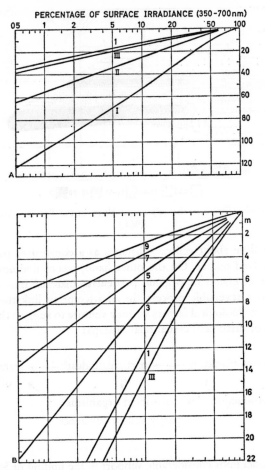

Fig.81. Depth profiles of percentage of surface downward irradiance (350—700 nm) for different water types.

particle content which is obviously due to phytoplankton or remnants of phytoplankton (JERLOV, 1953a).

Among the dissolved substances only yellow substance plays an important optical role. It is manifest that the wavelength selective absorption due to particles and yellow substance determines the transmittance of daylight and ultimately the colour of the sea. So far

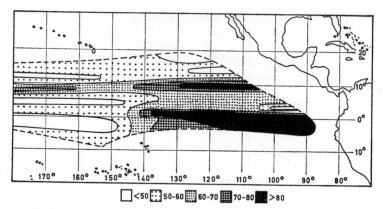

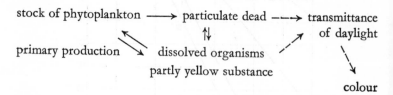

Fig.82. Particle content in the uppermost 50 m in the Pacific. (After Jerlov, 1964.)

we know little about yellow substance as a constituent part of the total dissolved matter. On the other hand, recent findings indicate that the conversion of organic particulate material into dissolved material is a reversible process. In an attempt to link the physical factors to the biological factors we may venture to suggest the following chain of direct and casual relationships:

stock of phytoplankton ⟶ particulate dead –⟶ transmittance
of daylight
primary production   dissolved organisms
partly yellow substance

colour

Such a model finds considerable support in the finding of Steemann Nielsen (1963) that the regional distribution of colour in the South Atlantic according to Schott's chart conforms in considerable detail to the observed regional distribution of primary production.

Quanta meter

The nature of photosynthesis as a quantum process suggests that light measurements in photosynthetic studies should be made in terms of number of quanta within a specified spectral range. This desideratum was recognized by Working Group 15 of the International Association of Physical Oceanography (IAPO) and the Special Committee on Oceanographic Research (SCOR). Chief object of its activity is to recommend an adequate meter for determining number of quanta and amount of energy in the interval 350–700 nm.

Absorption measurements

In laboratory studies of absorption spectra for translucent biological material it is desirable to bring out a strong absorption effect. The discussion in Chapter 3 maintains that a part of the transmitted light is direct and has not been scattered by suspended particles; the scattering, on the other hand, is chiefly due to diffraction at small angles and to refraction and reflection at greater angles. Since refraction is associated with absorption, a scattering cone of considerable angle should be recorded in order to improve the absorption effect. This condition is simply fulfilled by placing a diffusing glass before or after the sample cell. This principle long utilized in the Zeiss—Pulfrich photometer has been investigated by Shibata (1958). Murchio and Allen (1962) stress the fact that a similar high resolution is attained by using a wide beam. Yentsch (1962) has applied Shibata's method on natural plankton populations, obtaining excellent absorption reliefs as evidenced in Fig.83.

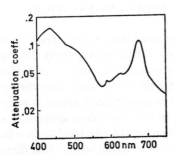

Fig.83. Attenuation spectrum of sea water suspension of *Phaeodactylum tricornutum*. Opal glass technique. (After Yentsch, 1962.)

BIOLUMINESCENCE

The generation of light or luminescence is a common characteristic of marine fauna. The activity of many organisms in the sea is controlled by the ambient light emanating from sun and sky, and the diurnal migration of the sonic scattering layers occurs according to changes in the ambient light level. Animals with sensitive eyes may perceive daylight at 1,000 m in the clearest waters and may detect luminescent flashes at distances of 40 m (CLARKE and DENTON, 1962). The complicated photic relation between migration, amount of luminescent flashing and ambient light changes cannot be discussed in the present context. Interested readers are referred, for instance, to the publications of BODEN and KAMPA (1964) and CLARKE and KELLY (1965).

Biologists have contributed considerable data about irradiance in the sea, especially for deep strata. This information is incorporated in the discussion of irradiance distribution (Chapter 10). It may be added that the proper functioning of meters specialized for measuring bioluminescence requires high sensitivity, great speed and preferably logarithmic response as the flashes are quite intense (CLARKE and HUBBARD, 1959). In deep layers it is often difficult to distinguish the biological and the physical phenomenon, since bioluminescence creates a background of light which mixes with the ambient light penetrating from surface.

ANIMAL ORIENTATION

It has been demonstrated that certain aquatic animals can use the sun for visual navigation (WATERMAN, 1959). This specific ability of determining direction in the sea involves an internal clock mechanism which compensates for the sun's movements through the sky. The usefulness of the sun as an accurate compass is somewhat restricted by the fact that the in situ sun seldom appears as an image but is disintegrated in a glitter pattern which subtends a fairly large angle. On the other hand, recent research testifies that directionality (in the apparent direction of the sun) of the radiance distribution persists down to greater depths than hitherto anticipated.

An exciting aspect of visual orientation in the sea concerns the polarization of underwater light. There is now conclusive evidence that in arthropods and even in cephalopods the plane of oscillation (e-vector) of linearly polarized light in the sea is perceived by a visual mechanism different from that which senses radiance patterns (WATERMAN, 1959; JANDER et al., 1963). The fact that polarization is an environmental factor adds further importance to such measurements.

REFERENCES

AGERONOV, V. K., 1964. On the daily fluctuations of radiant energy of the sun in the layers of the ocean in relation to its optical density. (7th cruise of S. R. ship "Mikhail Lomonosov"). *Tr. Morsk. Gidrofiz. Issled., Akad. Nauk S.S.S.R.*, 29: 76—83.

AHLQUIST, C. D., 1965. Strålningsenergins (från sol och himmel) fördelning i N. Östersjön, Ålandshav och S. Bottenhavet. Unpublished.

ALBRECHT, F., 1936. Ein Strahlungsbilanzmesser zur Messung des Strahlungshaushaltes von Oberflächen. *Meteorol. Z.*, 50: 62.

ANDERSON, E. R., 1954. Energy-budget studies. In: *Water Loss Investigations: Lake Hefner Studies — U.S., Geol. Surv., Profess. Papers*, 269: 71—117.

ANONYMOUS, 1957. International Lighting Vocabulary — *Comm. Intern. Eclairage, Publ.*, 1(1): 136 pp.

ARMSTRONG, F. A. J. and BOALCH, G. T., 1961. Ultraviolet absorption of sea water and its volatile components. *Union Géod. Géophys. Intern., Monographie*, 10: 63—66.

ASHLEY, L. E. and COBB, C. M., 1958. Single particle scattering functions for latex spheres in water. *J. Opt. Soc. Am.*, 48: 261.

ATKINS, W. R. G. and POOLE, H. H., 1933. The photo-electric measurement of penetration of light of various wavelengths into the sea and the physiological bearing of the results. *Phil. Trans. Roy. Soc. London, Ser.B*, 222: 129.

ATKINS, W. R. G. and POOLE, H. H., 1940. A cubical photometer for studying the angular distribution of submarine daylight. *J. Marine Biol. Assoc. U.K.*, 24: 271—281.

ATKINS, W. R. G. and POOLE, H. H., 1952. An experimental study of the scattering of light by natural waters. *Proc. Roy. Soc. (London), Ser.B*, 140: 321—338.

ATKINS, W. R. G. and POOLE, H. H., 1954. The angular scattering of blue, green, and red light by sea water. *Sci. Proc. Roy. Dublin Soc.*, 26: 313—323.

ATKINS, W. R. G. and POOLE, H. H., 1958. Cube photometer measurements of the angular distribution of submarine daylight and the total submarine illumination. *J. Conseil, Conseil Perm. Intern. Exploration Mer*, 23: 327—336.

BALL, T. F. and LaFOND, E. C., 1964. Turbidity of water off Mission Beach. In: *Physical Aspects of Light in the Sea*. Univ. Hawaii Press, Honolulu, Hawaii, pp.37—44.

BAUER, D. et IVANOFF, A., 1965. Au sujet de la mesure du coefficient de diffusion de la lumière par les eaux de mer pour des angles compris entre 14° et 1° 30'. *Compt. Rend.*, 260: 631—634.

BAUER, D. et MOREL, A., 1967. Étude aux petits angles de l'indicatrice de diffusion de la lumière par les eaux de mer. *Ann. Géophys.*, 23: 109–123.

BEIN, W., 1935. *Veröffentl. Inst. Meeresk. Berlin*, 28: 36.

BERGER, F., 1961. Über den "Taucheffekt" bei der Lichtmessung über und unter Wasser. *Arch. Meteorol. Wien, Ser.B*, 11: 224—240.

BEUTELL, R. G. and BREWER, A. W., 1949. Instruments for the measurement of the visual range. *J. Sci. Instr.*, 26: 357.

BLOUIN, F. et LENOBLE, J., 1962. Étude expérimentale des diffusions multiples de la lumière cas d'un milieu absorbant. *Rev. Opt.*, 12: 615—620.

BODEN, B. P., 1961. Twilight irradiance in the sea. *Union Géod. Géophys. Intern., Monographie*, 10: 96—101.

BODEN, B. P. and KAMPA, E. M., 1964. Planktonic bioluminescence. In: H. BARNES (Editor), *Oceanography and Marine Biology*. Hafner, New York, N.Y., 2: 341—372.

BODEN, B. P., KAMPA, E. M. and SNODGRASS, J. M., 1960. Underwater daylight measurements in the Bay of Biscay. *J. Marine Biol. Assoc. U.K.*, 39: 227—238.

BORN, M., 1963. Betrachtungen zur Farbenlehre. *Naturwissenschaften*, 50: 29—39.

BUNSEN, R., 1847. Blaue Farbe des Wassers und Eises. *Jahresber. Fortschr. Chem.*, 1847: 1236.

BURT, W. V., 1954a. Albedo over wind-roughened water. *J. Meteorol.*, 11: 283—290.

BURT, W. V., 1954b. Specific scattering by uniform minerogenic suspensions. *Tellus*, 6: 229—231.

BURT, W. V., 1955. Distribution of suspended materials in Chesapeake Bay. *J. Marine Res.*, 14: 47—62.

BURT, W. V., 1956. A light-scattering diagram. *J. Marine Res.*, 15: 76—80.

BURT, W. V., 1958. Selective transmission of light in tropical Pacific waters. *Deep-Sea Res.*, 5: 51—61.

CHANDRASEKHAR, S., 1950. *Radiative Transfer*. Oxford Univ. Press, London, 393 pp.

CHANU, J., 1959. Extraction de la substance jaune dans les eaux côtières. *Rev. Opt.*, 38: 569.

CLARKE, G. L. 1933. Observations on the penetration of daylight into mid-Atlantic and coastal waters. *Biol. Bull.*, 65: 317.

CLARKE, G. L. and DENTON, E. J., 1962. Light and animal life. In: M. N. HILL (General Editor), *The Sea, Ideas and Observations on Progress in the Study of the Seas*. Interscience, New York, N.Y., 1: 456—468.

CLARKE, G. L. and HUBBARD, C. J., 1959. Quantitative records of the luminescent flashing of oceanic animals at great depths. *Limnol. Oceanog.*, 4: 163—180.

CLARKE, G. L. and JAMES, H. R., 1939. Laboratory analysis of the selective absorption of light by sea water. *J. Opt. Soc. Am.*, 29: 43—55.

CLARKE, G. L. and KELLY, M. G., 1964. Variation in transparency and in bioluminescence on longitudinal transects in the western Indian ocean. *Bull. Inst. Oceanog. Monaco*, 64: 20 pp.

CLARKE, G. L. and KELLY, M. G., 1965. Diurnal changes in bioluminescence of oceanic organisms. *Limnol. Oceanog.*, 10: R54—R66.

CLARKE, G. L. and WERTHEIM, G. K., 1956. Measurements of illumination at great depths and at night in the Atlantic Ocean by means of a new bathyphotometer. *Deep-Sea Res.*, 3: 189—205.

COLLINS, J. R., 1925. A new infra-red absorption band of liquid water at 2.52 μ. *Phys. Rev.*, 55: 470—472.

COMMITTEE ON COLORIMETRY, 1966. *The Science of Color*, 6th ed. Opt. Soc. Am., Washington, D.C., 385 pp.

COOPER, L. H. N., 1961. Comparison between three methods of measuring underwater illumination in coastal waters. *J. Marine Biol. Assoc. U.K.*, 41: 535—550.

COUSTEAU, J.-Y., JAUSSERAN, C., LABAN, A. et LIBERMAN, M., 1964. Mesure de l'absorption dans l'eau de mer, de la lumière émise, par une source artificielle, à diverses profondeurs, verticalement et horizontalement. *Bull. Inst. Océanog. Monaco*, 63: 17 pp.

COX, C. and MUNK, W., 1956. Slopes of the sea surface deduced from photographs of sun glitter. *Bull. Scripps Inst. Oceanog. Univ. Calif.*, 6: 401—488.

CURRIE, R. I. and DRAPER, L., 1961. Time-integrated measurements of submarine irradiance. *Nature*, 191: 661—662.

CURCIO, J. A. and PETTY, C. C., 1951. The near infrared absorption spectrum of liquid water. *J. Opt. Soc. Am.*, 41: 302—304.

DAWSON, L. H. and HULBURT, E. O., 1937. The scattering of light by water. *J. Opt. Soc. Am.*, 27: 199—201.

DAWSON, L. H. and HULBURT, E. O., 1941. Angular distribution of light scattered in liquids. *J. Opt. Soc. Am.*, 31: 554—558.

DEIRMENDJAN, D., 1963. Scattering and polarization properties of poly-dispersed suspensions with partial absorption. In: *I.C.E.S. Electromagnetic Scattering*. Pergamon, London, 5: 171—189.

DERA, J., 1963. Sonda do badan uwarstwienia mas wodnych w morzu. *Acta Geophys. Polon.*, 11: 179—185.

DERA, J., 1965. Niektore Właściwości Optyczne Wód Zatoki Gdańskiej Jako Wskaźniki Struktury Jej Mas Wodnych. *Acta Geophys. Polon.*, 13: 15—39.

DUNTLEY, S. Q., 1948. The reduction of apparent contrast by the atmosphere. *J. Opt. Soc. Am.*, 38: 179—191.

DUNTLEY, S. Q., 1952. *The Visibility of Submerged Objects*. Visibility Laboratory, Mass. Inst. Technol., Cambridge, Mass., 74 pp.

DUNTLEY, S. Q., 1963. Light in the sea. *J. Opt. Soc. Am.*, 53: 214—233.

DUNTLEY, S. Q., UHL, R. J., AUSTIN, R. W., BOILEAU, A. R. and TYLER, J. E., 1955. An underwater photometer. *J. Opt. Soc. Am.*, 45: 904 (A).

DUNTLEY, S. Q., BOILEAU, A. R. and PREISENDORFER, R. W., 1957. Image transmission by the troposphere, I. *J. Opt. Soc. Am.*, 47: 499—506.

DUURSMA, E. K., 1960. *Dissolved Organic Carbon, Nitrogen and Phosphorus in the Sea*. Vrije Universiteit, Amsterdam, 147 pp.

DUURSMA, E. K. et ROMMETS, J. W., 1961. Interprétation mathématique de la fluorescence des eaux douces, saumâtres et marines. *Neth. J. Sea Res.*, 1: 391—405.

EINSTEIN, A., 1910. Theorie der Opaleszenz von homogenen Flüssigkeiten und Flüssigkeitsgemischen in der Nähe des kritischen Zustandes. *Ann. Physik*, 33: 1275.

FALLER, A. J., 1958. An optical method for the measurement of surface water in the laboratory. *Trans. Am. Geophys. Union*, 39: 716.

FOGG, G. E. and BOALCH, G. T., 1958. Extracellular products in pure cultures of a brown alga. *Nature*, 181: 789—790.

FORŠ, L. F., 1954. Otraženie solnečnoj radiacii ot vodnoj poverchnosti ozer. *Tr. Lab. Ozeroved., Akad. Nauk S.S.S.R.*, 3: 3—22.

FUKUDA, M., 1958. Design of an improved turbidity meter. *Bull. Fac. Fisheries, Hokkaido Univ.*, 9: 66—72.

FUKUDA, M., 1960. Transparency measurements in the Baltic Sea. *Medd. Oceanog. Inst. Göteborg*, 27: 1—18.

GERSHUN, A., 1936. O fotometrii mutnykk sredin. *Tr. Gos. Okeanogr. Inst.*, 11: 99.

GERSHUN, A., 1939. The light field. *J. Math. Phys.*, 18: 51—151.

GRIŠČENKO, D. L., 1959. Zavistimost' Albedo Morja ot Vysoty solnca i volnenija morskoj poverchnosti. *Glavnaja Geofis. Observ. A. I. Boejkova*, 80: 32—38.

GUMPRECHT, R. O. and SLIEPCEVICH, C. M., 1953. Scattering of light by large spherical particles. *J. Opt. Soc. Am.*, 57: 90—94.

HANAOKA, T., FURUKUWA, A. and NOGAMI, K., 1960. Studies on suspended matter in the sea, 4. On the relation between suspension factor, extinction coefficient and turbidity. *Bull. Japan. Soc. Sci. Fisheries*, 26: 469—471.

HART, T. J., 1966. Some observations on the relative abundance of marine phytoplankton populations in nature. In: H. BARNES (Editor), *Some Contemporary Studies in Marine Science*. Allen and Unwin, London, pp.375—395.

HARTEL, W., 1940. Zur Theorie der Lichtstreuung durch trübe Schichten, besonders Trübgläser. *Licht*, 10: 141.

HINZPETER, H., 1962. Messungen der Streufunktion und der Polarisation des Meerwassers. *Kieler Meeresforsch.*, 18: 36—41.

HISHIDA, K., 1953. Physical studies on the turbidity in sea water, with special reference to the relation of radiant energy. *J. Oceanog. Soc. Japan*, 9: 143—181.

HISHIDA, K. and KISHINO, M., 1965. On the albedo of radiation of the sea surface. *J. Oceanog. Soc. Japan*, 21: 148—153.

HODKINSON, J. R., 1963. Light scattering and extinction by irregular particles larger than the wavelength. In: M. KERKER (Editor), *I.C.E.S. Electromagnetic Scattering*. Pergamon, London, 5: 87—100.

HOLMES, R. W. and SNODGRASS, J. M., 1961. A multiple-detector irradiance meter and electronic depth-sensing unit for use in biological oceanography. *J. Marine Res.*, 19: 40—56.

HUBBARD, C. J., 1956. A wide-range, high-speed bathyphotometer. *U.S. Naval Res., Woods Hole Oceanog. Inst., Ref. No. 56—68*, 15 pp. (unpublished).

HUBBARD, C. J., 1958. Measurement of spectral distribution of light underwater. *U.S. Naval Res., Woods Hole Oceanog. Inst., Ref. No. 58—6*, 15 pp. (unpublished).

HULBURT, E. O., 1934. The polarization of light at sea. *J. Opt. Soc. Am.*, 24: 35—42.

HULBURT, E. O., 1945. Optics of distilled and natural water. *J. Opt. Soc. Am.*, 35: 698—705.

INOUE, N., NISHIZAWA, S. and FUKUDA, M., 1955. The perfection of a turbidity meter and the photographic study of suspended matter and plankton in the sea using an undersea observation chamber. *Proc. U.N.E.S.C.O. Symp. Phys. Oceanog.*, *Tokyo, 1955*, pp.53—58.

IVANOFF, A., 1956. Étude de pénétration de la lumière dans la mer. *Ann. Géophys.*, 12: 32—44.

IVANOFF, A., 1957a. Contribution à l'étude des propriétés optique de l'eau de mer en Bretagne et en Corse, et la théorie de la polarisation sous-marine. *Ann. Géophys.*, 13: 22—53.

IVANOFF, A., 1957b. Un polarimètre sous-marin à cellule photoélectrique, premiers résultats obtenus. *Bull. Inform. Comité Central Océanog. Étude Côtes*, 9: 491—499.

IVANOFF, A., 1957c. Au sujet de la visibilité des objets immergés. *Bull. Inform. Comité Central Océanog. Étude Côtes*, 9: 270—283.

IVANOFF, A., 1959. Optical method of investigation of the ocean. The $p—\beta$ diagram. *J. Opt. Soc. Am.*, 49: 103—104.

IVANOFF, A., 1960a. Au sujet des perfectionnements apportés à l'étude de la lumière diffusée par des échantillons d'eau de mer, et des résultats ainsi obtenus au large de Monaco. *Compt. Rend.*, 250. 736—738.

IVANOFF, A., 1960b. Au sujet de la teneur de l'eau en particules en suspension au voisinage immédiat du fond de la mer. *Compt. Rend.*, 250: 1881—1883.

IVANOFF, A., 1961. Quelques résultats concernant les propriétés diffusantes des eaux de mer. *Union Géod. Géophys. Intern.*, *Monographie*, 10: 45—51.

IVANOFF, A., 1964. Measurements at sea of water samples. In: *Physical Aspects of Light in the Sea*. Univ. Hawaii Press, Honolulu, Hawaii, pp.11—17.

IVANOFF, A. et LENOBLE, J., 1957. Au sujet de l'influence de l'ouverture du faisceau incident sur le facteur de dépolarisation de la lumière diffusée par les molécules. *Compt. Rend.*, 244: 329—331.

IVANOFF, A. et MOREL, A., 1964. Au sujet de l'indicatrice de diffusion des eaux de mer. *Compt. Rend.*, 258: 2873—2876.

IVANOFF, A. et MOREUIL, J. L., 1963. Au sujet de la répartition des luminances sous-marines au voisinage immédiat de la direction apparente du soleil. *Compt. Rend.*, 256: 4711—4712.

IVANOFF, A. and WATERMAN, T. H., 1958a. Elliptical polarization of submarine illumination. *J. Marine Res.*, 16: 255—282.

IVANOFF, A. and WATERMAN, T. H., 1958b. Factors, mainly depth and wavelength, affecting the degree of underwater light polarization. *J. Marine Res.*, 16: 283—307.

IVANOFF, A., JERLOV, N. and WATERMAN, T. H., 1961. A comparative study of irradiance, beam transmittance and scattering in the sea near Bermuda. *Limnol. Oceanog.*, 6: 129—148.

JAMES, H. R. and BIRGE, E. A., 1938. A laboratory study of the absorption of light by lake waters. *Trans. Wisc. Acad. Sci.*, 31: 154 pp.

JANDER, R., DAUMER, K. and WATERMAN, T. H., 1963. Polarized light observation by two Hawaiian Decapod cephalopods. *Z. Vergleich. Physiol.*, 46: 383—394.

JERLOV, N. G., 1951. Optical studies of ocean water. *Rept. Swedish Deep-Sea Expedition*, 3: 1—59.

JERLOV, N. G., 1953a. Particle distribution in the ocean. *Rept. Swedish Deep-Sea Expedition*, 3: 73—97.

JERLOV, N. G., 1953b. Influence of suspended and dissolved matter on the transparency of sea water. *Tellus*, 5: 59—65.

JERLOV, N. G., 1955a. Factors influencing the transparency of the Baltic waters. *Medd. Oceanog. Inst. Göteborg*, 25: 19 pp.

JERLOV, N. G., 1955b. The particulate matter in the sea as determined by means of the Tyndall meter. *Tellus*, 7: 218—225.

JERLOV, N. G., 1957. A transparency-meter for ocean water. *Tellus*, 9: 229—233.

JERLOV, N. G., 1958. Distribution of suspended material in the Adriatic Sea. *Arch. Oceanog. Limnol.*, 11: 227—250.

JERLOV, N. G., 1959. Maxima in the vertical distribution of particles in the sea. *Deep-Sea Res.*, 5: 178—184.

JERLOV, N. G., 1961. Optical measurements in the eastern North Atlantic. *Medd. Oceanog. Inst. Göteborg, Ser. B*, 8: 40 pp.

JERLOV, N. G., 1963. Optical oceanography. *Oceanog. Marine Biol. Ann. Rev.*, 1: 89—114.

JERLOV, N. G., 1964. Optical classification of ocean water. In: *Physical Aspects of Light in the Sea*. Univ. Hawaii Press. Honolulu, Hawaii, pp.45—49.

JERLOV, N. G., 1965. The evolution of the instrumental technique in underwater optics. In: M. SEARS (Editor), *Progress in Oceanography*. Pergamon, New York, N.Y., 3: 149—154.

JERLOV, N. G. and FUKUDA, M., 1960. Radiance distribution in the upper layers of the sea. *Tellus*, 12: 348—355.

JERLOV, N. G. and KOCZY, F., 1951. Photographic measurements of daylight in deep water. *Rept. Swedish Deep-Sea Expedition*, 3: 61—69.

JERLOV, N. G. and KULLENBERG, B., 1953. The Tyndall effect of uniform minerogenic suspensions. *Tellus*, 5: 306—307.

JERLOV (JOHNSON), N. G. and LILJEQUIST, G., 1938. On the angular distribution of submarine daylight and the total submarine illumination. *Svenska Hydrograf. Biol. Komm. Skrifter, Ny Ser. Hydrog.*, 14: 15 pp.

JERLOV, N. G. and NYGÅRD, K., 1961. Measured irradiance. In: *Optical Measurements in the Eastern North Atlantic — Medd. Oceanog. Inst. Göteborg, Ser.B*, 8: 22—29.

JERLOV (JOHNSON), N. G. and OLSSON, H., 1944. On the standardziation of photoelectric elements by means of solar radiation. The total energy of incident radiation computed from records with photo-electric elements. *Statens Meteorol. Hydrograf. Anstalt, Comm. Ser. Papers*, 47: 1—24.

JONES, D. and WILLS, M. S., 1956. The attenuation of light in sea and estuarine waters in relation to the concentration of suspended solid matter. *J. Marine Biol. Assoc. U.K.*, 35: 431—444.

JOSEPH, J., 1949a. Durchsichtigkeitsmessungen im Meere im ultra-violetten Spektralbereich. *Deut. Hydrograph. Z.*, 2: 212—218.

JOSEPH, J., 1949b. Über die Messung des "Vertikalen Extinktions-koeffizienten". *Deut. Hydrograph. Z.*, 2: 255—267.

JOSEPH, J., 1950. Untersuchungen über Ober- und Unterlichtmessungen im Meere und über ihren Zusammenhang mit Durchsichtigkeitsmessungen. *Deut. Hydrograph. Z.*, 3: 324—335.

JOSEPH, J., 1955. Extinction measurements to indicate distribution and transport of watermasses. *Proc. U.N.E.S.C.O. Symp. Phys. Oceanog., Tokyo, 1955*, pp. 59—75.

JOSEPH, J., 1959. Uber die vertikalen Temperatur- und Trübungsregistrierungen in einer 500 m mächtigen Deckschicht des nördlichen nordatlantischen Ozeans. *Deut. Hydrograph. Z.*, 3: 48 pp.

JOSEPH, J., 1961. Trübungs- und Temperatur-Verteilung auf den Stationen und Schnitten von V.F.S. "Gauss" etc., 1957—1958. *Deut. Hydrograph. Z.*, 5.

JOSEPH, J. und SENDNER, H., 1958. Über die horizontale Diffusion im Meere. *Deut. Hydrograph. Z.*, 11: 49—77.

KALLE, K., 1938. Zum Problem der Meereswasserfarbe. *Ann. Hydrol. Marine Mitt.*, 66: 1—13.

KALLE, K., 1939a. Bericht 2. Teilfahrt der deutsche nordatlantische Expedition "Meteor". V. Die chemischen Arbeiten auf der "Meteor"-Fahrt, Januar bis Mai 1938. *Ann. Hydrograph. Maritimen Meteorol., Beih. Z.*, 1939 (Januar): 23—30.

KALLE, K., 1939b. Die Farbe des Meeres. *Rappt. Procès-Verbaux Réunions, Conseil Perm. Intern. Exploration Mer*, 109: 96—105.

KALLE, K., 1949. Fluoreszenz und Gelbstoff im Bottnischen und Finnischen Meerbusen. *Deut. Hydrograph. Z.*, 2: 117—124.

KALLE, K., 1961. What do we know about the "Gelbstoff"? *Union Géod. Géophys. Intern., Monographie*, 10: 59—62.

KALLE, K., 1962. Über die gelösten organischen Komponenten im Meerwasser. *Kieler Meeresforsch.*, 18: 128—131.

KALLE, K., 1966. The problem of the Gelbstoff in the sea. *Oceanog. Marine Biol. Ann. Rev.*, 4: 91—104.

KAMPA, E. M., 1961. Daylight penetration measurements in three oceans. *Union Géod. Géophys. Intern., Monographie*, 10: 91—96.

KETCHUM, B. H. and SHONTING, D. H., 1958. Optical studies of particulate matter in the sea. *Woods Hole Oceanog. Inst., Ref. No. 58—15*, 28 pp.

KIMBALL, H. H., 1924. Records of total solar radiation intensity and their relation to daylight intensity. *Monthly Weather Rev.*, 52: 475.

KNESTRICK, G. L., CURCIO, J. A. and ROCKMAN, A. G., 1965. *Comparison of Underwater Attenuation of Laser with Nonlaser Light*. U.S. Naval Res. Lab., Washington, D.C., 8 pp.

KNUDSEN, M., 1922. On measurement of penetration of light into the sea. *Conseil Perm. Intern. Exploration Mer, Publ. Circ.*, 76: 16 pp.

KOZLYANINOV, M. V., 1957. New instrument for measuring the optical properties of sea water. *Tr. Inst. Okeanol., Akad. Nauk S.S.S.R.*, 25: 134.

KOZLYANINOV, M. V., 1959. Nekotorye voprosy metodiki gidrooptičeskich issledovanij vodoemov. *Tr. VI Sov. Probl. Biol. Vnutrennich Vod. 10—19 June, 1957. Zool. Inst. Biol. Vodochran., Akad. Nauk S.S.S.R.*, pp.546—552.

KOZLYANINOV, M. V., 1960. O nekotorych optičeskich charakteristikach vod central'noj casti Tichogo okeana. *Tr. Inst. Okeanol., Akad. Nauk S.S.S.R.*, 40: 167—174.

KOZLYANINOV, M. V., 1961. Rukovodstvo po gidrooptičeskim izmerenijam v more. *Tr. Inst. Okeanol., Akad. Nauk S.S.S.R.*, 47: 37—79.

KOZLYANINOV, M. V. and OVCHINNIKOV, I. M., 1961. On the relation of transparency with the nature of the currents of the northeastern Pacific. *Tr. Inst. Okeanol., Akad. Nauk S.S.S.R.*, 45: 102–112.

KOZLYANINOV, M. V. and PELEVIN, V. N., 1966. On the application of a one-dimensional approximation in the investigation of the propagation of optical radiation in the sea. *U.S. Dept. Comm., Joint Publ. Res. Ser., Rept.*, 36: 54–63.

KOZLYANINOV, M. V. and SEMENCHENKO, I. V., 1962. Measuring of the eigen-luminosity of the sea from an aeroplane. *Tr. Inst. Okeanol., Akad. Nauk S.S.S.R.*, 55: 62–66.

KREY, J., 1961. Der Detritus im Meere. *J. Conseil, Conseil Perm. Intern. Exploration Mer*, 26: 263–280.

KULLENBERG, G., 1966. Internal report. Univ. of Copenhagen.

KULLENBERG, G., 1967a. In situ measurements of horizontal and vertical diffusion in the thermocline in Swedish coastal waters. Univ. of Copenhagen, in press.

KULLENBERG, G., 1967b. Internal report. Univ. of Copenhagen.

LAUSCHER, F., 1947. Zur Strahlungstheorie der Hydrosphäre. *Sitzber. Akad. Wiss. Wien, Abt. IIA*, 155: 281.

LAUSCHER, F., 1955. Optik der Gewässer. Sonnen und Himmelstrahlung im Meer und in Gewässern. In: *Handbuch der Geophysik*. Springer, Berlin–Heidelberg–Wien, 7: 723–768.

LE GRAND, Y., 1939. La pénétration de la lumière dans la mer. *Ann. Inst. Océanog.*, 19: 393–436.

LE GRAND, Y., 1954. Recherches récentes dans le domaine de l'optique de la mer. *Compt. Rend. Études Océanog.*, 1: 1–4.

LE GRAND, M. Y. et LENOBLE, J., 1955. Sur quelques mesures de la pénétration du rayonnement ultraviolet dans les eaux de Dinard. *Bull. Lab. Maritime Dinard*, 41: 22–23.

LE GRAND, Y., LENOBLE, J. et SAINT-GUILY, M., 1954. Étude de la pénétration de l'ultraviolet dans la mer. *Ann. Géophys.*, 10: 59–63.

LENOBLE, J., 1956a. Sur le rôle des principaux sels dans l'absorption ultraviolette de l'eau de mer. *Compt. Rend.*, 242: 806–808.

LENOBLE, J., 1956b. Angular distribution of submarine daylight in deep water. *Nature*, 178: 756–757.

LENOBLE, J., 1956c. Étude de la pénétration de l'ultraviolet dans la mer. *Ann. Géophys.*, 12: 16–31.

LENOBLE, J., 1956d. Remarque sur la couleur de la mer. *Compt. Rend.*, 242: 662–664.

LENOBLE, J., 1957a. Spectrophotomètre photoélectrique sous-marin. *Bull. Inform. Comité Central. Océanog. Étude Côtes*, 9: 551–564.

LENOBLE, J., 1957b. Etude de la pénétration du rayonnement ultraviolet naturel dans la mer. *Bull. Inform. Comité Central Océanog. Étude Côtes*, 9: 9–20.

LENOBLE, J., 1958a. Pénétration du rayonnement ultraviolet dans la mer. *Ann. Inst. Océanog.*, 34: 297–308.

LENOBLE, J., 1958b. Sur l'état de polarisation du rayonnement diffus aux grandes profondeurs dans un milieu suivant la loi de Rayleigh. *Compt. Rend.*, 246: 924–927.

LENOBLE, J., 1961a. Application de la méthode des harmoniques sphériques au cas de la diffusion anisotrope. *Compt. Rend.*, 252: 2087–2089.

LENOBLE, J., 1961b. Theoretical study of transfer of radiation in the sea and verification on a reduced model. *Union Géod. Géophys. Intern., Monographie*, 10: 30—37.

LENOBLE, J., 1961c. Application de la méthode des harmoniques sphériques à l'étude de l'état de polarisation du rayonnement diffus. *Compt. Rend.*, 252: 3562—3564.

LENOBLE, J., 1963. Essai d'une méthode générale pour l'introduction des fonctions X et Y de Chandrasekhar dans le cas de la diffusion anisotrope. *Compt. Rend.*, 256: 4638—4640.

LENOBLE, J. et SAINT-GUILLY, B., 1955. Sur l'absorption du rayonnement par l'eau distillée. *Compt. Rend.*, 240: 954—955.

LISSBERGER, P. H. and WILCOCK, W. L., 1959. Properties of all-dielectric interference filters, 2. Filters in parallel beams of light incident obliquely and in convergent beams. *J. Opt. Soc. Am.*, 49: 126—130.

LISITSYN, A. P., 1961. *Raspredelenie i Sostav Vzveschennogo Materiale v Moryakh i Okeanakh*. Sovremennye Osadki Morei i Okeanov (Tr. Soveskehaniya 24—27 maya 1960 g), Moskva, pp.175—232.

LÜNEBURG, H., 1939. Hydrochemische Untersuchungen in der Elbemündung. *Archiv Deut. Seewarte*, 59(5).

LÜNEBURG, H., 1953. Beiträge zur Hydrographie der Wesermündung. Die Probleme der Sinkstoffverteilung in der Wesermündung. *Veröffentl. Inst. Meeresforsch., Bremerhaven*, 2: 15.

MALMBERG, SV. Å., 1964. Transparency measurements in the Skagerrak. *Medd. Oceanog. Inst. Göteborg*, 31: 18 pp.

MATTHÄUS, W., 1965. Ein verbessertes Messverfahren für ozeanographische Lichtextinktionsmessungen in situ. *Beitr. Meeresk.*, 16: 31—36.

MIDDLETON, W. E. K., 1952. *Vision through the Atmosphere*. Univ. Toronto Press, Toronto, Ont., 250 pp.

MIE, G., 1908. Beiträge zur Optik trüber Medien, speziell kolloidalen Metalllösungen. *Ann. Physik.*, 25: 377.

MOON, P. and SPENCER, D. E., 1942. Illumination from a non-uniform sky. *Illum. Eng.*, 37: 707—726.

MOREL, A., 1965. Résultats expérimentaux concernant la pénétration de la lumière du jour dans les eaux méditerranéennes. *Cahier Océanog.*, 17: 177—184.

MOREL, A., 1966. Étude expérimentale de la diffusion de la lumière par l'eau, les solutions de chlorure de sodium et l'eau de mer optiquement pures. *J. Chim. Phys.*, 10: 1359—1366.

MUKAI, M., 1959. Intensity of illumination at a small plate lowered in lake or marine water. *J. Oceanog. Soc. Japan*, 15: 1—10.

MULLAMAA, Y. R., 1964a. Penetration of direct radiation into the sea. *Izv. Akad. Nauk S.S.S.R., Ser. Geofiz.*, 8: 1259—1268.

MULLAMAA, Y. R., 1964b. The reflection of direct radiation from an ocean surface. *Izv. Akad. Nauk S.S.S.R., Ser. Geofiz.*, 8: 1232—1246.

MURCHIO, J. C. and ALLEN, M. B., 1962. Measurement of absorption spectra of chlorophyll in algal cell suspensions. *Photochem. Photobiol.*, 1: 259—266.

NEIBURGER, M., 1948. The reflection of diffuse radiation by the sea surface. *Am. Geophys. Union, Trans.*, 29: 647—652.

NEUMANN, G. and HOLLMAN, R., 1961. On the albedo of the sea surface. *Union Géod. Géophys. Intern., Monographie*, 10: 72—83.

NEUYMIN, G. G. and PARAMONOV, A. N., 1961. Fotoelektričeskij fotometr dlja izmerenija podvodnoj osveščennosti. *Okeanologiya*, 1: 904—910.

NEUYMIN, G. G. and SOROKINA, N. A., 1964. Ob optičeskich rassenvajuscich slojach v more. *Tr. Inst. Okeanol., Akad. Nauk S.S.S.R.*, 4: 51—54.

NEUYMIN, G. G., SOROKINA, N. A., PARAMONOV, A. N. and PROSCHCHIN, V. N., 1964. Hydrophysical investigations. Some results of the optical investigations in the northern part of the Atlantic Ocean (7th cruise of S.R. ship "Mikhail Lomonosov"). *Tr. Morsk. Gidrofiz. Issled. Akad. Nauk S.S.S.R.*, 29: 64—75.

NISHIZAWA, S. and INOUE, N., 1958. Turbidity distribution and its relation to some oceanographical factors in the eastern China Sea in the late summer of 1956. *Records Oceanog. Works Japan, Spec. No.*, 2: 101—115.

NISHIZAWA, S. and INOUE, N., 1964. Vertical turbidity variation in shallow oceanic water column. In: M. SEARS (Editor), *Studies in Oceanography*. Pergamon, New York, N.Y., pp.279—287.

NISHIZAWA, S., FUKUDA, M. and INOUE, N., 1954. Photographic study of suspended matter and plankton in the sea. *Bull. Fac. Fisheries, Hokkaido Univ.*, 5: 36—40.

NISHIZAWA, S., INOUE, N. and AKIBA, Y., 1959. Turbidity distribution in the subarctic water of the North Pacific in the summer of 1957. *Records Oceanog. Works Japan, Spec. No.*, 3: 231—241.

OCHAKOVSKY, YU. E., 1960. Photoelektrisches Photometer — Durchsichtigkeitsmesser mit dem Registrier-Apparat Modell FPM-57. *Tr. Inst. Okeanol., Akad. Nauk S.S.S.R.*, 39: 39—42.

OCHAKOVSKY, YU. E., 1966a. On the dependence of the total attenuation coefficient upon suspensions in the sea. *U.S. Dept. Comm., Joint Publ. Res. Ser., Rept.*, 36(816): 16—24.

OCHAKOVSKY, YU. E., 1966b. On the comparison of measured and calculated scattering indicatrices of sea water. *U.S. Dept. Comm., Joint Publ. Res. Ser., Rept.*, 36(816): 98—105.

PANGONIS, W. J. and HELLER, W., 1960. *Angular Scattering Functions for Spherical Particles*. Wayne State Univ. Press, Detroit, Mich., 228 pp.

PARAMONOV, A. N., 1964. Morskoj impul'snyj fotometr-prozracnomer. Princip raboty. Elektriceskaja schema i konstrukcija pribora. *Tr. Inst. Okeanol., Akad. Nauk S.S.S.R.*, 2: 314—320.

PARAMONOV, A. N., 1965. The distribution pattern of suspended matter in the Black Sea — some measurement results. *Tr. Inst. Okeanol., Akad. Nauk S.S.S.R.*, 5: 64—67.

PARSONS, T. R., 1963. Suspended organic matter in sea water. In: M. SEARS (Editor), *Progress in Oceanography*. Pergamon, New York, N.Y., 1: 205—239.

PAVLOV, V. M., 1961. Poljarizacija estestvennogo sveta v more. *Tr. Inst. Okeanol., Akad. Nauk S.S.S.R.*, 47: 80—91.

PAVLOV, V. M. and GRECHUSHNIKOV, B. N., 1966. Some aspects of the theory of daylight polarization in the sea. *U.S. Dept. Comm., Joint Publ. Res. Ser., Rept.*, 36 (816): 25—44.

PELEVIN, V. N., 1966. Some experimental results of the determination of the true absorption coefficient of light at sea. *U.S. Dept. Comm., Joint Publ. Res. Ser., Rept.*, 36 (816): 45—53.

PETTERSSON, H., 1934. Scattering and extinction of light in sea water. *Medd. Oceanog. Inst. Göteborg*, 9: 1—16.

PETTERSSON, H., 1936. Das Licht im Meer. *Meteorol. Z., Bioklimatol. Beibl.*, 3.

PETTERSSON, H. and LANDBERG, S., 1934. Submarine daylight. *Medd. Oceanog. Inst. Göteborg*, 6: 1—13.

PEYROT, P., 1938. Contrôle expérimental des formules théoriques. *Ann. Physik*, 9: 394—405.

PICKARD, G. L. and GIOVANDO, L. F., 1960. Some observations of turbidity in British Columbia inlets. *Limnol. Oceanog.*, 5: 162—170.

POOLE, H. H., 1936. The photo-electric measurement of submarine illumination in off-shore waters. *J. Conseil, Conseil Perm. Intern. Exploration Mer*, 1: 12 pp.

POOLE, H. H., 1945. The angular distribution of submarine daylight in deep water. *Sci. Proc. Roy. Dublin Soc.*, 24: 29—42.

PREISENDORFER, R. W., 1957. Exact reflectance under a cardioidal luminance distribution. *Quart. J. Roy. Meteorol. Soc.*, 83: 540.

PREISENDORFER, R. W., 1958. Directly observable quantities for light fields in natural hydrosols. *Scripps Inst. Oceanog. Univ. Calif., Ref. 58—46*, 29 pp.

PREISENDORFER, R. W., 1959. Theoretical proof of the existence of characteristic diffuse light in natural waters. *J. Marine Res.*, 18: 1—9.

PREISENDORFER, R. W., 1960. *Recommendation on the Standardization of Concepts, Terminology, and Notation of Hydrologic Optics.* Scripps Inst. Oceanog. Univ. Calif., La Jolla, Calif., 96 pp.

PREISENDORFER, R. W., 1961. Application of radiative transfer theory to light measurements in the sea. *Union Géod. Géophys. Inst., Monographie*, 10: 11—30.

PREISENDORFER, R. W., 1964. A model for radiant distribution in natural hydrosols. In: *Physical Aspects of Light in the Sea.* Univ. Hawaii Press, Honolulu, Hawaii, pp.51—60.

PREISENDORFER, R. W., 1965. *Radiative Transfer on Discrete Spaces.* Pergamon, New York, N.Y., 462 pp.

PRITCHARD, B. S. and ELLIOTT, W. C., 1960. Two instruments for atmospheric optics measurements. *J. Opt. Soc. Am.*, 50: 191—202.

RAMAN, C. V., 1922. On the molecular scattering of light in water and the colour of the sea. *Proc. Roy. Soc. (London), Ser.A*, 101: 64—79.

RAYLEIGH, LORD, 1871. On the scattering of light by small particles. *Phil. Mag.*, 41: 447—454.

REPLOGLE JR., F. S. and STEINER, I. B., 1965. Resolution measurements in natural water. *J. Opt. Soc. Am.*, 55: 1149—1151.

RICHARDSON, W. S. and SHONTING, D. H., 1957. Particulate matter in the sea. *Woods Hole Oceanog. Inst., Ref. 58—15*, 9 pp. (unpublished).

RILEY, G. A., STOMMEL, H. and BUMPUS, D. F., 1949. Quantitative ecology of the plankton of the western North Atlantic. *Bull. Bingham Oceanog. Coll.*, 12: 1—169.

SASAKI, T., OSHIBA, G., WATANABE, S. and OKAMI, N., 1952. On the submarine visibility by sealed-beam headlight bulb. *Bull. Japan. Soc. Sci. Fisheries*, 19: 216—222.

SASAKI, T., OKAMI, N., WATANABE, S. and OSHIBA, G., 1955. Measurements of the angular distribution of submarine daylight. *J. Sci. Res. Inst., Tokyo*, 49: 103—106.

SASAKI, T., OKAMI, N., OSHIBA, G. and WATANABE, S., 1958a. Spectral energy distribution of submarine daylight off Kii peninsula — in relation to the investigation of oceanic productivity. *Records Oceanog. Works Japan, Spec. No.*, 2: 119—128.

SASAKI, T., OSHIBA, G., WATANABE, S. and OKAMI, N., 1958b. A submersible turbiditymeter. *Records Oceanog. Works Japan, Spec. No.*, 2: 116—119.

SASAKI, T., WATANABE, S., OSHIBA, G. and OKAMI, N., 1958c. Measurements of angular distribution of submarine daylight by means of a new instrument. *J. Oceanog. Soc. Japan*, 14: 47—52.

SASAKI, T., OKAMI, N., WATANABE, S. and OSHIBA, G., 1959. Measurements of submarine light polarization. *Records Oceanog. Works Japan, Spec. No.*, 5: 91—97.

SASAKI, T., WATANABE, S., OSHIBA, G. and OKAMI, N., 1960. Measurements of perpendicular and horizontal angular distributions of submarine daylight by means of a new remote control instrument. *Records Oceanog. Works Japan, Spec. No.*, 4: 197—205.

SASAKI, T., OKAMI, N., OSHIBA, G. and WATANABE, S., 1962a. Studies on suspended particles in deep sea water. *Sci. Papers, Inst. Phys. Chem. Res. (Tokyo)*, 56: 77—83.

SASAKI, T., WATANABE, S., OSHIBA, G., OKAMI, N. and KAJIHARA, M., 1962b. On the instrument for measuring angular distribution of underwater radiance. *Bull. Japan. Soc. Sci. Fisheries*, 28: 489—496.

SAUBERER, F. und RUTTNER, F., 1941. *Die Strahlungsverhältnisse der Binnengewässer*. Akademie Verlag, Berlin, 240 S.

SCHELLENBERG, G., 1963. Die Grundgleichungen der Optik der Hydrosphäre. *Beitr. Geophys.*, 72: 315—327.

SCHEMAINDA, R., 1962. Ergebnisse einiger Durchsichtigkeitsmessungen im Raum der ozeanischen Polarfront westlich von Spitzbergen. *Beitr. Meeresk.*, 6: 45—54.

SCHENCK JR., H., 1957. On the focusing of sunlight by ocean waves. *J. Opt. Soc. Am.*, 47: 653—657.

SCHOOLEY, A. H., 1961. Relationship between surface slope, average facet size and facet flatness tolerance of a wind-disturbed water surface. *J. Geophys. Res.*, 66: 157—162.

SEKERA, Z., 1957. Polarization of skylight. In: *Handbuch der Physik*. Springer, Berlin—Heidelberg—Vienna, S.288—328.

SHAPIRO, J., 1957. Chemical and biological studies on the yellow organic acids of lake water. *Limnol. Oceanog.*, 2: 161—179.

SHELFORD, V. E. and GAIL, F. W., 1922. A study of light penetration into seawater made with the Kunz photoelectric cell with particular reference to the distribution of plants. *Publ. Puget Sound Biol. Sta.*, 3: 141—176.

SHIBATA, K., 1958. Spectrophotometry of intact biological materials. *J. Biochem. (Tokyo)*, 45: 599—604.

SHOULEIKIN, W., 1923. On the colour of the sea. *Phys. Rev.*, 22: 86—100.

SHOULEIKIN, W., 1941. *Fizika Moria (Physics of the Sea)*. Izd. Akad. Nauk S.S.S.R., Moscow, 833 pp.

SMOLUCHOWSKI, M., 1908. Molekular-kinetische Theorie der Opaleszenz von Gasen im kritischen Zustande, sowie einiger verwandter Erscheinungen. *Ann. Physik*, 25: 205.

SNODGRASS, J. M., 1961. Some recent developments in oceanographic instrumentation. *Union Géod. Géophys. Intern., Monographie*, 10: 83—91.

SOKOLOV, O. A., 1963. Visual underwater observations on the fifth voyage of the submarine "Severyanka". *Deep-Sea Res.*, 10: 70—72.

SPIELHAUS, A. F., 1965. *Observations of Light Scattering in Sea Water*. Office Naval Res., Washington, D.C., Dept. Geol. Geophys., Mass. Inst. Technol., Cambridge, Mass., 242 pp.

STAMM, G. L. and LANGEL, R. A., 1961. Some spectral irradiance measurements of upwelling natural light of the east coast of the United States. *J. Opt. Soc. Am.*, 51: 1090—1094.

STEEMANN NIELSEN, E., 1963. Fertility of the ocean. In: M. N. HILL (General Editor), *The Sea, Ideas and Observations on Progress in the Study of the Seas*. Interscience, New York, N.Y., 2: 129—164.

STELENAU, A., 1961. Über die Reflexion der Sonnenstrahlung an Wasserflächen und ihre Bedeutung für das Strahlungsklima von Seeufern. *Beitr. Geophys.*, 70: 90—123.

STRICKLAND, J. D. H., 1958. Solar radiation penetrating the ocean. A review of requirements, data and methods of measurement with particular reference to photosynthetic productivity. *J. Fisheries Res. Board Can.*, 15: 453—493.

SULLIVAN, S. A., 1963. Experimental study of the absorption in distilled water, artificial sea water, and heavy water in the visible region of the spectrum. *J. Opt. Soc. Am.*, 53: 962—967.

SUTCLIFFE, W. H., BAYLOR, E. R. and MENZEL, D. W., 1963. Sea surface chemistry and Langmuir circulation. *Deep-Sea Res.*, 10: 233—243.

TAKENOUTI, Y., 1940. Angular distribution of submarine solar radiations and the effect of altitude of the sun upon the vertical extinction coefficient. *Bull. Japan. Soc. Sci. Fisheries*, 8: 213—219.

TAKENOUTI, Y., 1949. On the diffusion-ratio of under-water illuminations. *Oceanog. Mag.*, 1: 43—48.

TAYLOR, A. H. and KERR, G. P., 1941. The distribution of energy in the visible spectrum of daylight. *J. Opt. Soc. Am.*, 31: 3—8.

TIMOFEEVA, V. A., 1951a. On the problem of scattering of luminosity in the sea. *Dokl. Akad. Nauk S.S.S.R.*, 76: 831—833.

TIMOFEEVA, V. A., 1951b. Distribution of luminosity in strongly scattering media. *Dokl. Akad. Nauk S.S.S.R.*, 76: 677—680.

TIMOFEEVA, V. A., 1957. The dependence of the shape of a polar luminance diagram on the ratio of the absorption and scattering coefficients. *Dokl. Akad. Nauk S.S.S.R.*, 113: 556—559.

TIMOFEEVA, V. A., 1960. Instrument for determining the attenuation coefficient of directed light in the sea. *Sov. Oceanog. 1962 Ser.*, 4: 79—83.

TIMOFEEVA, V. A., 1961. On the problem of the polarization of light in turbid media. *Izv. Akad. Nauk S.S.S.R., Ser. Geofiz.*, 5: 766—774.

TIMOFEEVA, V. A., 1962. Spatial distribution of the degree of polarization of natural light in the sea. *Izv. Akad. Nauk S.S.S.R., Ser. Geofiz.*, 6: 1843—1851.

TYLER, J. E., 1958. Comparison of light distribution above and below water. *J. Marine Res.*, 16: 96—99.

TYLER, J. E., 1959. Natural water as a monochromator. *Limnol. Oceanog.*, 4: 102—105.

TYLER, J. E., 1960a. Observed and computed path radiance in the underwater light field. *J. Marine Res.*, 18: 157—167.

TYLER, J. E., 1960b. Radiance distribution as a function of depth in an underwater environment. *Bull. Scripps Inst. Oceanog. Univ. Calif.*, 7: 363—412.

TYLER, J. E., 1961a. Scattering properties of distilled and natural waters. *Limnol. Oceanog.*, 6: 451—456.

TYLER, J. E., 1961b. Sun-altitude effect on the distribution of underwater light. *Limnol. Oceanog.*, 6: 24—25.

TYLER, J. E., 1961c. Measurements of the scattering properties of hydrosols. *J. Opt. Soc. Am.*, 51: 1289—1293.

TYLER, J.E., 1963a. Design theory for a submersible scattering meter. *Appl.Opt.*, 2: 245—248.

TYLER, J. E., 1963b. Estimation of per cent polarization in deep oceanic water. *J. Marine Res.*, 21: 102—109.

TYLER, J. E., 1964. Colour of the ocean. *Nature*, 202: 1262—1264.

TYLER, J. E. and AUSTIN, R. W., 1964. A scattering meter for deep water. *Appl. Opt.*, 3: 613—620.

TYLER, J. E. and HOWERTON, R., 1962. Instrument for measuring the forward scattering coefficient of sea water. *Limnol. Oceanog.*, 7: 393—395.

TYLER, J. E. and RICHARDSON, W. H., 1958. Nephelometer for the measurement of volume scattering function in situ. *J. Opt. Soc. Am.*, 48: 354—357.

TYLER, J. E. and SHAULES, A., 1964. Irradiance on a flat object underwater. *Appl. Opt.*, 3: 105—110.

TYLER, J. E. and SMITH, R. C., 1966. Submersible spectroradiometer. *J. Opt. Soc. Am.*, 56: 1390—1396.

TYLER, J. E., RICHARDSON, W. H., and HOLMES, R. W., 1959. Method for obtaining the optical properties of large bodies of water. *J. Geophys. Res.*, 64: 667—673.

UTTERBACK, C. L. and BOYLE, T. W., 1933. Light penetration in the waters of San Juan Archipelago. *J. Opt. Soc. Am.*, 23: 1.

VAN DE HULST, H. C., 1957. *Light Scattering by Small Particles*. Wiley, New York, N.Y., 470 pp.

VOITOV, V. I., 1964. Optičeskie charakteristiki vodnych mass kak pokazateli procesov turbulentnogo peremešivanija v more. *Tr. Inst. Okeanol., Akad. Nauk S.S.S.R.*, 4: 386—394.

WATERMAN, T. H., 1954. Polarization patterns in submarine illumination. *Science*, 120: 927—932.

WATERMAN, T. H., 1955. Polarization of scattered sunlight in deep water. In: *Papers in Marine Biology and Oceanography*. Pergamon, London, pp.426—434.

WATERMAN, T. H., 1959. Animal navigation in the sea. *Gunma J. Med. Sci.*, 8: 243—262.

WATERMAN, T. H. and WESTELL, W. E., 1956. Quantitative effect of the sun's position on submarine light polarization. *J. Marine Res.*, 15: 149—169.

WATTENBERG, H., 1938. Untersuchungen über Durchsichtigkeit und Farbe des Seewassers, I. *Kieler Meeresforsch.*, 2.

WESTLAKE, D. F., 1965. Some problems in the measurement of radiation under water: a review. *Photochem. Photobiol.*, 4: 849—868.

WHITNEY, L. V., 1938. Transmission of solar energy and the scattering produced by suspension in lake waters. *Trans. Wisc. Acad. Sci. Arts Letters*, 31: 201—221.

WHITNEY, L. V., 1941. The angular distribution of characteristic diffuse light in natural waters. *J. Marine Res.*, 4: 122.

WILLIAMS, J., 1955. Chesapeake Bay Inst., Ref. No. 55-4: 35 pp.

WOODWARD, D. H., 1964. Multiple light scattering by spherical dielectric particles. *J. Opt. Soc. Am.*, 54: 1325—1331.

WYRTKI, K., 1950. Über die Beziehungen zwischen Trübung und ozeanographischem Aufbau. *Kieler Meeresforsch., Inst. Meeresk.*, 7: 87—107.

WYRTKI, K., 1953. Ergebnisse über die Verteilung der Trübung in Küstennahe. *Veröffentl. Inst. Meeresforsch., Bremerhaven*, 2: 269—278.

WYRTKI, K., 1960. Optical measurements in the Coral and Solomon seas. *Union Géod. Géophys. Intern., Monographie*, 10: 51—59.

YENTSCH, C. S., 1960. The influence of phytoplankton pigments on the colour of the sea water. *Deep-Sea Res.*, 7: 1—9.

YENTSCH, C. S., 1962. Measurement of visible light absorption by particulate matter in the ocean. *Limnol. Oceanog.*, 7: 207—217.

YENTSCH, C. S. and REICHERT, C. A., 1962. The interrelationship between water-soluble yellow substances and chloroplastic pigments in marine algae. *Botan. Marina*, 3: 65—74.

YENTSCH, C. S. and RYTHER, J. H., 1959. Absorption curves of acetone extracts of deep water particulate matter. *Deep-Sea Res.*, 6: 72—74.

INDEX

WIDENER COLLEGE
WOLFGRAM
LIBRARY
CHESTER, PA.